Jane's
Citizen's Safety Guide

First Edition

Sonayia Shepherd
John B. Copenhaver
Robert Marston Fanney
Rennie Campbell
Adrian Dwyer
Jessica Duda

Published by Jane's Information Group
Sentinel House
163 Brighton Road, Coulsdon
Surrey, CR5 2YH, UK
Tel: +44 (00 8700 3700
Fax: +44 (0) 8763 1006
e-mail: info@janes.com

Printed in the United States

Registered with the Library of Congress

Cataloging-in-Publication Data available upon request

ISBN 0710626614

Editorial and Project Management
Content Developer: Jessica Duda

Editorial
Content Developer: Rob Fanney
Consultancy Manager: Rennie Campbell
Consultancy Manager: Jim Tinsley
Content Developer: Mary Dinh
Content Developer: Seth Drewry
Sub-editor: Julia Goodwin, Eagle Design & Management

Graphic Design

Layout
Graphic Designer: Bethany Hackmann
Content Developer: Jessica Duda

Photo editor
Content Developer: Jessica Duda

Illustrations
Graphic Designer: Bethany Hackmann

Front Cover
Graphic Designer: Bethany Hackmann

Production
Page Layout: Jennifer Stamper, Independent Consultant
Global Production Services Manager: Jane Lawrence
Production Services Mac Team Leader: Natalie Wilson

Administration
Content Development Manager: Ian Synge
Business Development Director: Michael Dell
Chief Executive Officer: Alfred Rolington

Publisher's Note

Jane's would like to thank the authors of *Jane's Citizen's Safety Guide*:

Sonayia (Sony) Shepherd, lead editor and writer of *Jane's Citizen's Safety Guide*, currently serves as Bio-terrorism Exercise Coordinator for a state public health agency. She previously served as School Safety Coordinator and as the State Anti-terrorism Planner for the Georgia Emergency Management Agency - Office of the Governor. Ms. Shepherd serves as a crisis responder for several national crisis teams. She has authored and co-authored 14 books on emergency preparedness and safety-related issues and writes the "Sony Says" monthly column for *Campus Safety Journal*. She is a regular presenter at state, national and international professional conferences.

John B. Copenhaver is Chair and CEO of Disaster Recovery Institute (DRI) International, a non-profit business continuity certification and education organization. He contributed to the following chapters: Why Should I Use This Planning Guide, Government Protection: Who Does What and What to Expect, Personal Disaster Preparedness, Security in the Workplace, Natural Disasters and Accidents and After an Emergency: What Do I Do Now. He directed the federal government emergency response to 58 presidential disaster declarations and was appointed by President Clinton to serve as the head of the largest Federal Emergency Management Agency (FEMA) regional office. He has extensive experience in corporate contingency planning and emergency response as former Senior Advisor, IBM International Crisis Response Team and Director of Business Continuity Services, BellSouth Business Systems.

Robert Marston Fanney is Content Developer at Jane's Information Group. He is author of the Staying Alert and Reporting Incidents chapter and contributor to the Weapons of Mass Destruction and natural disaster sections. He is the editorial project manager for the forthcoming titles: *Jane's Safe Schools Planning Guide for All Hazards, Jane's School Safety Handbook Second Edition* and *Jane's Teacher's Safety Handbook*. He was editor of *Jane's Chem-bio Handbook Second Edition, Jane's Chem-bio Handbook International, Jane's ChemBio Web* and *Jane's World Insurgency and Terrorism*. He is a former Intelligence Analyst, National Guardsman as well as Police Officer for Naval Security Force (NSF) division of Naval Criminal Investigative Service (NCIS).

Rennie Campbell is Consultancy Manager at Jane's Information Group. He is author of the Street Smarts and Travel Security chapter and contributor to the Security in the Workplace chapter and radiological weapons section. He was also editorial and project manager for *Jane's School Safety Handbook, Jane's Workplace Security Handbook, Jane's Mass Casualty Handbook: Hospital* and *Jane's Mass Casualty Handbook: Pre-hospital*.

Adrian Dwyer is a Counter-terrorism Advisor to the British Transport Police. He contributed to the the Weapons of Mass Destruction section. He is a former British Army bomb disposal officer and high-risk search advisor as well as lead editor and writer of *Jane's Chem-bio Handbook* and contributor to *Jane's Chemical-Biological Defense Guidebook*.

Jessica Duda is Content Developer for Jane's Information Group. She is contributing editor and project manager of *Jane's Citizen's Safety Guide*. She wrote the sections on children, hazardous materials, public affairs and media, insurance and private contractors as well as contributed to the Security in the Workplace chapter. She was editorial and project manager for *Jane's Crisis Communications Handbook* and an editor of *Jane's Workplace Security Handbook* and *Jane's Unconventional Weapons Response Handbook*.

The following expert review panel leant their expertise and experience in emergency preparedness, response and recovery issues during the development of the guide:

Dr. Susan Allan MD, JD, MPH
Health Director, Arlington County Department of Human Services, Arlington, VA and contributor of *Jane's Mass Casualty: Pre-Hospital*

Ken Alibek
Executive Director for Education, George Mason University National Center for Biodefense and contributor to *Jane's Chem-Biological Defence Guidebook* and *Jane's Chem-Bio Handbook*

Dr. Steven M. Becker
Associate Professor of Public Health, Director, Social, Behavioral & Public Policy Unit, Center for Disaster Preparedness; Lister Hill Scholar in Health Policy, The University of Alabama at Birmingham and reviewer for *Jane's Mass Casualty Handbook: Hospital*

Len Cross
Retired FBI agent who conducted terrorism crime scene investigations and Manager, Maritime Security Department at Han-Padron Associates, Tampa, FL

Roger Davies
Former commander of the Northern Ireland Bomb Disposal Unit; member of the UN Terrorism Prevention Branch Roster of Experts; Director of Hazard Management Solutions Ltd; *Jane's Intelligence Review* correspondent and reviewer of *Jane's Unconventional Weapons Handbook*

LTC Robert Domenici
Program Coordinator, Homeland Security Exercise & Evaluation New York State WMD Task Force; former Military Advisor to New York and reviewer for *Jane's Chem-bio Handbook, 2nd Edition* and *Jane's Crisis Communications Handbook*

Mike Dorn
Executive Director, Safe Havens International, Inc. and contributor to *Jane's School Safety* series

Captain Louie Fernandez
Senior Bureau Chief, Miami-Dade Fire Rescue & Office of Emergency Management Public Affairs and lead editor of *Jane's Crisis Communications Handbook*

David A. Kuhn
Advanced law enforcement and first responder trainer on terrorism incident response and WMD for local, state, and federal agencies in the State of Florida; contributor to *Jane's Unconventional Weapons Response Handbook, Jane's Mass Casualty Handbooks, Workplace Security Handbook* and correspondent for *Jane's Intelligence Review*

Peter La Duca
Senior Manager, Health & Safety Training and Information Service at the Board of Cooperative Educational Services of Nassau County, New York

Herbert Lattimore, Jr
Counter-Terrorism Planner, Department of Military Affairs and Public Safety, Office of Emergency Services, Charleston, WV

Richard Pilch
Scientist-in-Residence, Center for Nonproliferation Studies, Monterrey Institute for International Studies, Monterrey, CA

Bonnie Piper
Deputy Director of Media Relations, US Environmental Protection Agency, Washington, DC and reviewer for *Jane's Crisis Communications Handbook*

John Rinard
EMT-P, LP, WMD EMS Supervisor, Emergency Services Training Institute, Texas Engineering Extension Service, Texas A&M University System

Joan F. Roche
Director of Training, Massachusetts Emergency Management Agency

Gary Tuchman
National Correspondent, CNN, Altanta, GA and reviewer for *Jane's Crisis Communications Handbook*

Paul Viollis
President, Risk Control Strategies, Inc. and lead editor of *Jane's Workplace Security Handbook*

Marleen Wong
Director, Crisis Counseling and Intervention Services Los Angeles Unified School District; Director, School Crisis and Intervention Unit National Center for Child Traumatic Stress UCLA and Duke University; and contributor to *Jane's School Safety* series

Special Thanks

The following provided valuable feedback and support for the development of the guide:

Steve Allen, Babak Akhlaghi, Dawn Brito, Matthew Brown, Collette Conconi, Clara Dixon, the Duda family, Chris Evenden, Kelvin Gosnell, Glenn Griffith, Scott Hayes, Dr. Henrike Paepcke, George Paul, Robert Petty, Linda Van Buren, Jeanie Wine and Carn Wright

IMPORTANT

Jane's Citizen's Safety Guide is designed to assist people of varying needs to make calm, quick and safe decisions regarding potential threats at home, school and the workplace as well as within their community. As such, it should be used in addition to an additional advice from emergency services as well as other appropriate literature.

This book is based on current research, knowledge and understanding, and to the best of the authors' ability the material is current and valid. While the authors, editors, publishers and Jane's Information Group have made reasonable efforts to ensure the accuracy of the information contained herein, they cannot be held responsible for any errors found in this book. The authors, editors, publishers and Jane's Information Group do not bear any responsibility or liability for the information contained herein or for any uses to which it may be put.

While reasonable care has been taken in the compilation and editing of this title, it should be recognized that the contents are for information purposes only and do not constitute any guidance to the use of the equipment described herein or its rendering safe. Jane's Information Group cannot accept any responsibility for any accident, injury, loss or damage arising from use of this information.

Table of Contents

Chapter 4 > School Safety: Have You Done Your Homework?

Chapter 5 > *Security in the Workplace*

Chapter 6 > Street Smarts and Travel Safety

Part Three **Reporting and Response**
Chapter 7 > Staying Alert and Reporting Incidents

Chapter 8 > *Natural Disasters and Accidents*

Chapter 9 > *Hazardous Materials and Weapons of Mass Destruction*

Part Four **Recovery**
Chapter 10 > After an Emergency: What Do I Do Now?

Chapter 11 > Psychological Effects of Emergencies

Jane's Consultancy

Customized Security Intelligence and Response for Your Requirements

Jane's prides itself on its globally recognized reputation for independent, impartial, accurate and timely security information and analysis, established through our authoritative publications and services on defense, security and international terrorist and criminal activity.

Building on this expertise, Jane's Consultancy provides targeted, customized and confidential solutions that combine Jane's expertise in both threat assessment and mitigation to meet your specific emergency preparedness, response and recovery requirements.

Jane's Consultancy applies an understanding of the motivations, capabilities and methodologies of potential threats to your region, and creates a tailored, comprehensive and robust response plan to mitigate those threats. Key services include:

- Hazard/threat assessments, including 'red teaming'
- Developing an Emergency Operations Plan
- Developing Incident Management/Command Systems
- Conducting training and exercises, including desktop and full scenarios

For more information, contact your local Jane's representative or simply visit http://consultancy.janes.com or email: consultancy@janes.com

Part 1
Risks and Protection

If you prepare with your family, friends, neighbors and co-workers, emergencies will be easier to manage.
2003/0562452

Part One **Chapter 1**

Why Should I Use This Planning Guide?

"Community disaster response is certainly not a new concept. The history of [America's] pioneers is filled with stories of neighbors helping neighbors and communities banding together in the face of adverse conditions," says Frank Lucier, retired Lieutenant from the San Francisco Fire Department, President of North American Emergency Management, Inc. and Executive Board member of the National Institute for Urban Search and Rescue.

Use your tools and resources to help yourself and others plan for emergencies.

Introduction

Emergencies can be overwhelming for everyone involved: victims, neighbors and first responders, such as police officers, fire fighters and paramedics. Those watching these events unfold on the 24-hour news coverage also become aware of the dangers around us. Some emergencies are out of our control, such as natural disasters. Others are the result of negligence or a lack of preparedness, such as school violence or terrorism. Believe or not, you have the power to protect yourself from emergencies and lessen their impact on you and your family.

Jane's Citizen's Safety Guide provides practical steps to help you and your family combine and apply first responder practices and street smart techniques to prevent, prepare and recover from emergencies.

Everyday risks

The world in which we live seems to grow more dangerous each day. More products that we regularly use cause cancer; the ozone layer is eroding and terrorism is rearing its ugly head in more places. Images of tragedy and loss bombard us on a daily basis. How much is hype and how much is real?

Chapter Overview

This chapter will provide you with a road map to use the emergency planning, prevention, response and recovery best practices in this guidebook:

- Everyday risks
- Where you can take control
- Emergency preparedness

Some natural disasters are anticipated and others occur within a moments notice. Know how to protect yourself and your home ahead of time. 2003/ 0562451

At More Or Less Risk?

People in the United States are living longer as Dr Susan Allen, Health Director of the Arlington County Department of Human Services in Virginia explains, "most of the increase [in life expectancy] came from safer food, water, work sites, houses and general environmental improvements — not from medical care as some may think. Overall, we are living longer than any generation in the past. We are less likely to die in infancy, while giving birth, on our jobs and even in our advanced years than ever."

In Your Neck of the Woods

Research the natural hazards in your area. One place to start is the US Geological Survey web site, Geographic Distribution of Major Hazards in the United States, located at www.usgs.gov/themes/hazards/html or call the public information line of your local emergency management agency.

In general, the risks we face increase in population growth, environmental changes and technological advancements. For example, suburban sprawl fueled the devastating impact of the 2003 California wildfires. Increased use of large vehicles requires more gasoline; thus fuel emissions as well as transportation of hazardous materials. The growing use of the Internet for commercial transactions can create a greater vulnerability to cyber terrorism.

Perception of risk largely depends on where you live, your age and lifestyle choices. If you ask your grandparents if we face more risks today, they will most likely say yes. To them, the world has changed dramatically and they now see more threatening images than when they were reaching adulthood. For people in their 20s, however, life doesn't seem to be as dangerous as for their grandparents.

What risks do you really face each day? What can you do to decrease the likelihood of such threats? How do you become ready to meet the risks of everyday life?

Travel near and away from home

While traveling in your community, on vacation or for work, you may encounter theft, violence and other emergencies. Do you know how to avoid pickpockets? Do your children know how to stay away from strangers? How can you prepare for a trip to protect your identity, financial and physical security? When traveling in a vehicle, train or airplane, do you know how to protect yourself from violence? See *Chapter 6: Street Smarts and Travel Safety* for tips on avoiding incidents while traveling in and outside of your community.

Natural disasters and accidents

The impact of natural disasters and accidents near your home — utilities and transport problems, hazardous household products or civil disturbance — largely depend on where you live. Some natural hazards can be predicted. The current weather technology allows for few surprises from some incidents, such as oncoming hurricanes. Large earthquakes can strike without any warning. Are you prepared natural disasters? Do you know the right places to shelter or evacuate during a tornado or a hurricane? Are you aware of hazards in your home, such as toxins in your cleaning products? Do you know what to do if a group of people near you create a civil disturbance? See *Chapter 8: Natural Disasters and Accidents* for planning, response and recovery steps you can take for natural hazards, mechanical accidents near and inside your home and civil disturbance.

Terrorism

No person is immune from terrorism but you can broadly figure out your risk. Over the past two years in particular, the government and media have focused more on the risk of terrorism. While the threat is real, the chances of being a victim of terrorism are much less than being in a car crash (1 in 6,745), in a fire (1 in 82,977) or struck by lighting (1 in 4,468,159) according to the Harvard Center for Risk Analysis. Therefore, the vast majority of the 292.6 million people living in America are not in immediate danger from terrorism.

Locations vulnerable to terrorism can be defined, despite the current belief that most areas are in danger. Broadly, terrorists seek areas or organizations that represent cultural, human, government/military or economic value. Most actions in life boil down to logistics and incentives. In turn, terrorists will look for the simplest way to inflict the most destruction or disruption in order to make their point heard. If an organization is difficult to infiltrate, terrorists will go to a less secure target or 'to the path of least resistance.' Instead of directing you to a specific chapter devoted to terrorism, this book focuses on sources of emergencies and how to respond because an accident and an act of terrorism could have the same effect. Whether an oil refinery accident or an attack, you would need to take the same steps to protect yourself against such a hazardous materials release.

Hazardous materials and Weapons of Mass Destruction

Much discussion has centered on the possibility of a Weapons of Mass Destruction (WMD) attack, which is broadly defined as an act that can inflict mass casualties usually involving chemical, biological, radiological or nuclear agents. What is more likely to occur, however, is a hazardous materials (HazMat) release; such as from a traffic accident causing a petroleum semi-truck to spill industrial chemicals. In all cases, do you know how protect yourself? Do you know when to remain indoors and when to evacuate a building and/or area? See *Chapter 9: Hazardous Materials and Weapons of Mass Destruction* to understand the dangers of these elements and how to protect yourself.

Physical and emotional impact of disasters

The impact of an emergency, especially a large-scale disaster may affect your home life in terms of your amenities and/or emotional health. In the short-term, your home may be without gas, electricity or water service. You may need to leave your home for a long period of time depending on the damage. Community-wide cleanup and reconstruction may take months to years to finish. Do you have enough food, water and supplies in your home to last you through an emergency? Are your personal documents, such as a will, social security cards, birth certificates, organized and in a safe place?

Path of Least Resistance

Terrorism experts conclude that terrorist groups seek to cause casualties, fear, panic, destruction and disruption. Experts also conclude that individuals and groups who have actually been able to inflict these terrible acts of physical and psychological violence commit and repeat these acts based on a certain formula. The circumstances and threats change, but the formula stays the same: target a location of value that is easy to reach and gives the 'biggest bang for the buck.' If a facility or area is not protected and is of human, cultural, economic or government value; terrorists create ways to cause harm to those areas. When their efforts fail, they do not repeat those tactics and therefore their methods can change over time. Just like companies, terrorist groups look at what others are doing to repeat the 'successful' missions and to avoid those that 'fail.' Overall, terrorists depend on a specific set of circumstances and must train to cause harm. They do not create terror out of thin air.

Emergencies can impact your community sometimes for months and even years. 2003/ 0562456

After emergencies, volunteer organizations like the Salvation Army help bring life back to normal. Source: FEMA Photo Archive. 2003/0562455

From The Front Porch

The area around your home could be your greatest security risk. "Like many young people in Washington, DC, I lived in a group house in a neighborhood teeming with restaurants, bars and clubs," says a Cleveland, Ohio transplant. "From the front porch of our house on Euclid Street, we saw a variety of events since the first group of six moved in during 1988. Parking fights, drug-related crimes, fires, home and store robberies, uninvited porch visitors and even shootings and a riot are a part of house history. The nearby crack and halfway houses seemed to be less threatening than talking to a stranger away from the porch. We didn't live in fear probably because these incidents didn't happen on a daily basis and thankfully none of us were harmed. Staying alert and ready to act made it manageable. For better or worse, these street scenes were a bit of a source of entertainment.

After three years and a pay increase, I moved into my own place in another neighborhood. When saying goodbye to the 12 year-old boy living with his family of six in the basement apartment, he said, 'Oh, you are moving there, you better be careful.' It took a year and a half to see a notable street scene and I do miss sitting on that front porch."

Do you have the right amount of insurance coverage for specific risks in your area, such as for flood damage? See *Chapter 10: After an Emergency: What Do I Do Now?* for suggestions to restore your routine when an emergency has affected your home and community.

Emergencies may also cause emotional trauma and the loss of a loved one. Do you know the emotional affects of disasters? Do you know how to protect yourself from restarting bad habits, such as drinking alcohol or smoking, after a stressful incident? Do you know how to discuss these issues with your children or help them recover from trauma? Are you aware of the community-wide impact of emergencies known as the *Five Stages of Crisis Recovery*? See *Chapter 11: Psychological Effects of Emergencies* to understand how disasters cause emotional trauma and the responses you and your children may experience.

Where you can take control

Home
Your home is probably where you spend most of your time and face the most risks. Familiarity doesn't breed contempt so much as it creates blind spots. Hazards unnoticeably start out small and grow into serious safety threats. At home, you deal with fire or heat when cooking, electricity and water while operating kitchen appliances. Most of the cleaning products you use can be hazardous to the eyes, respiratory and digestive systems. Have you eliminated as many health hazards as possible in your home? Do you have fire and carbon monoxide detectors — with charged batteries? Also, are your personal affairs organized in the event you have to evacuate or make an insurance claim or police report? See *Chapter 3: Personal Disaster Preparedness* to organize your home and personal affairs in the event of an emergency.

School
From time to time, children at or near their school find themselves in terrible situations due to either natural disasters, traffic accidents or violence. Are your school officials prepared to protect your children in the event of an emergency? Do you know where to pick up your children if an emergency happens while they are at school? Does the school have your contact information and/or instructions for any of your children's special needs? See *Chapter 4: School Safety: Have You Done Your Homework?* to learn about school safety planning for parents, children and school staff.

Work

Workers potentially face threats of armed robbery, co-worker and domestic violence as well as terrorism. Does your workplace have a designated crisis team to handle employee welfare in the event of an emergency? Does your employer provide information on safe ways to leave work? Have you given your employer family emergency contact information in the event an emergency keeps you from returning home on time? For more information on workplace security see *Chapter 5: Security in the Workplace.*

Emergency preparedness

Order in the chaos

Believe it or not, a certain order of events occurs during an emergency. First, confusion surrounds the scene and slowly evolves into some degree of order. First responders' arrival and reaction is critical as it affects the chain reaction of events — and media coverage of the situation. Events usually escalate as challenges continue to confront the response team — possibly attracting media speculation. Information is initially conflicting and tends to arrive in sudden bursts. Public interest soars initially, especially for reassurance, and then tends to diminish. External influence is unavoidable as reporters, politicians and others comment on the response and impact of the disaster. This in turn can influence your view of your own safety and faith in the government to resolve the situation. The following diagram shows how different groups of people come together during an emergency.

Diagram 1.1 Crisis group relationships

Source: CDC Emergency Risk Communications 2002

Build on what you know

More than likely you already have a pretty good idea of how to prepare for a disaster. After all, your instincts that have brought you this far. Also, local, state and federal government agencies continue to provide large amounts of information on disaster preparedness. You can build on your current knowledge base and seek input from disaster response agencies and organizations like the American Red Cross. Much of this book will sound like common sense — and not by accident. In an emergency situation, common sense, a cool head and a little planning will go a long way. Most people fear the unknown and learning how to protect yourself from a range of incidents can help reduce the fear that comes from not knowing what to do or how to help.

Emergency planning

Taking a short time — even a weekend — to understand how to protect yourself and recover from a disaster can help prevent panic.

For most people, disasters and family emergencies do not happen everyday. For this reason, people are taken by surprise or are unprepared to deal with the event and its consequences. Taking a short time — even a weekend — to understand how to protect yourself and recover from a disaster can prevent panic. Being prepared can help shield you from the negative effects of a family emergency, such as teaching your five-year old how to use her inhaler to deal with asthma while at school. In the event of a large-scale disaster, your preparedness will allow you to help others instead of worsening crisis. Applying the suggestions in this book to fit your life style is a way to start the process sooner rather than later.

Eight-step Plan to Emergency Preparedness

Use this outline to organize your disaster plan with your family and others involved in your life whether with your school, work and/or community.

1. Find out the risks in your area and government services available to help.
2. Create an emergency response plan with your family and friends while keeping in mind needs of your school, work and community.
3. Organize emergency supplies for home and on-the-go.
4. Repair and ready your home for likely risks.
5. Prepare personal affairs in the event you need to recover from an emergency.
6. Understand how to protect yourself from risks in your area.
7. Learn how emergencies impact your relationships and even your self-image and view of the world.
8. Find out how you can offer your skills to help others in need before, during and after emergencies.

See *Chapter 3: Personal Disaster Preparedness* on creating a disaster plan.

Take action: observe, decide, react

First responders use the same procedures for a variety of disasters and adapt them as the situation requires. You can also apply your planning efforts to small and large emergencies. While learning how to protect yourself from risks, keep in mind these three steps:

1. **Observe** the situation, taking in any unique or unusual circumstances.
2. **Decide** on what the appropriate response should be, if any.
3. **React** accordingly.

Know when to call on first responders for help and to move out of harm's way. 2003/ 0562454

Help first responders

Most damage from an emergency occurs within the first 15 minutes. Therefore, it is crucial for you to cooperate with first responders either by following their emergency instructions or those you have heard throughout your life. This book shows you how to be independent so that first responders can focus their limited time and resources to help people in life or death situations. The following are core principals to follow that will help first responders save lives and minimize further damage.

First responders are government officials responsible for public safety before, during and after emergencies.

- Prepare ahead of time as much as possible.
- Know when and who to call for help.
- Follow directions.
- Do not be a hero by putting yourself in harm's way.

This book occasionally refers to jargon typical in the emergency response arena. It will be helpful that you become familiar with key terms and definitions so that when you deal with emergency responders, you minimize the communication gap. *Chapter 2: Government Protection: Who Does What and What to Expect* explains how first response agencies work to protect you before, during and after emergencies. *Chapter 7: Staying Alert and Reporting Incidents* explains key terms to help you remember and explain important details of an emergency to the authorities.

Overall, use this book to learn what to expect, help you prepare, avoid danger and restore life to normal after an emergency. This book is not a self-defense guide or a first-aid manual. It is designed to teach you how to help yourself and to know when and what type of assistance to expect from the government, your school and/or employer. Consider *Jane's Citizen's Safety Guide* as a road map to self-empowerment to make quick, safe and effective decisions in a crisis.

Quiz yourself, family and friends

1. What factors affect potential risks in your life?

    A. Your age
    B. Your neighborhood
    C. Your lifestyle
    D. All of the above

2. What kinds of places do terrorists target?

3. What is the Eight-step Plan to Emergency Preparedness?

4. What three processes should you think of before responding to an emergency situation?

5. How can being prepared help first responders?

Find out the answers to the Chapter 1 quiz on page 200.

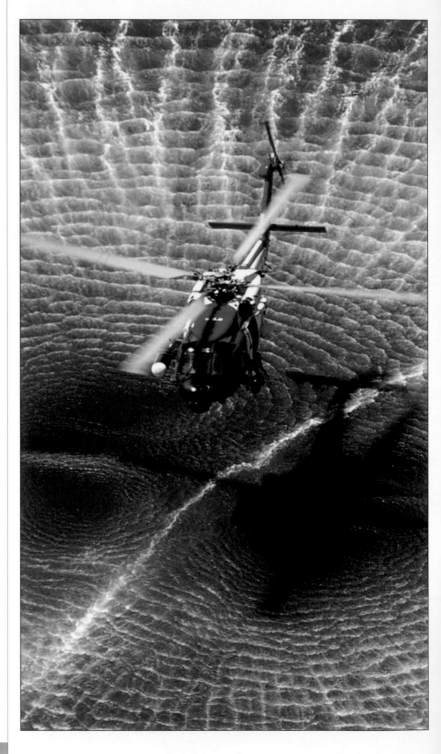

First responders across local, state, federal and military agencies plan to protect you before, during and after disasters. Pictured: US Coast Guard HH-60 Jayhawk recovery helicopter. Source: photo by PA2 Jacquelyn Zettle, USCG. 2003/0562467

Government Protection: Who Does What and What to Expect

"I can't guarantee there's going to be any event," said Dr. Keyes, a physician at Parkland Health and Hospital System in Dallas. "But it just seems like the risks are greater at this time. The biggest deterrent is to be ready for it."

by Matt Slagle, *Associated Press*, January 11, 2000

Introduction

On local, state and federal levels, a growing number of government agencies support emergency preparedness and response. Some provide direct support through services, such as fire protection, law enforcement, emergency medical service (EMS) and public health agencies. Others develop procedures to help emergency preparedness organizations coordinate their efforts in the event of a disaster. Lastly, others help citizens volunteer to help disaster victims and communities recover.

Local agencies

Responders and experts

Experts who prevent and respond to different types of disasters often are members of your local responder community. Most live in your region and therefore have a good understanding of the local geography and politics. Many of these experts have also witnessed the tragic effects of disasters, such as death, looting or widespread physical and psychological injuries. Because of their local knowledge and close ties to your region, they have a vested interest in the safety and welfare of the community. Responders can lead dangerous lives and self-sacrifice is a part of what they do every day to ensure that you can lead a safe and secure life.

Chapter Overview

This chapter describes the roles and responsibilities of emergency response agencies before, during and after incidents as well as how the media contributes.

- Local agencies
- State agencies
- Federal agencies
- How response agencies work together
- Media role in emergencies
- Local volunteer resources

Many fire services provide paramedic response during an emergency. Courtesy of Miami-Dade Fire Rescue. 2003/0562459

Most fire services also provide emergency medical service assistance by supporting EMS, hazardous materials (HazMat) as well as search and rescue response efforts.

Currently, volunteers make up 90 percent of fire services

Local fire services

Ongoing responsibilities

The local fire service provides fire protection, prevention and response support to communities. In addition, most fire services also provide emergency medical service assistance by providing or supporting EMS, hazardous materials (HazMat) as well as search and rescue response efforts. The fire services perform an essential, often life-saving role in most communities because many types of fires, such as automotive accidents, wildfires or building fires, occur relatively frequently.

During an incident

Currently, volunteers make up 90 percent of fire services and they are involved in the following activities in various ways:

- Fire prevention
- Arson/fire cause investigation
- Traffic accidents
- Urban and underwater search and rescue
- Civil defense
- High rise building rescue and protection against collapsed buildings
- Response to natural disasters: storms, floods and forest fires
- Medical response
- HazMat response

Fire services and WMD

In most communities, the fire department also responds to incidents involving toxic chemical, biological or radiological material, as well as Weapons of Mass Destruction (WMD)-related emergencies. The amount of training and equipment available in your locality will depend on local resources and on the risks in your area. Because not all local fire services have the same response capabilities, check your local fire department's website or call their information line to find out what kind of support they provide.

Local law enforcement

Ongoing responsibilities

The police also provide bomb squads that they either manage or request from the National Guard or other activity duty bomb disposal teams.

The police prevent and respond to emergencies in order to re-establish the peace. Police departments work to maintain order, apprehend and detain suspects, take reports from witnesses, control traffic, process and collect evidence, investigate crime scenes and evacuate areas. The police also provide bomb squads that they either manage or request from the National Guard or other activity duty bomb disposal teams.

During and after an incident

Police are often the first to arrive on the scene of a disaster as well as conduct first aid, perimeter control and apprehend suspected criminals. As all police are trained to provide first aid and CPR, they may often help victims before the fire department or EMS arrive. Generally, the police will provide the initial incident size-up and ensure other responders can arrive through safe routes to the disaster site. They isolate the crime scene by blocking off an area and redirecting traffic. Creating this 'secure perimeter' protects the victims, other citizens and the media from danger while providing first responders the space to do their jobs. Following an emergency, police also investigate crimes, provide victim/witness assistance maintain order and make arrests as necessary.

Police perform a variety of protection and investigative services before, during and after incidents. 2003/0562461

Types of police agencies

Although most law enforcement agencies have similar missions, such as protecting citizens, enforcing laws and providing services, differences exist among them.

Local or municipal police agencies protect and enforce laws mainly within the confines of their city or town. These law enforcement agencies may range from very small (fewer than 25 sworn officers serving populations under 25,000) to large cities and metropolitan areas with thousands of sworn officers serving millions of residents.

Police departments in different local, county and state jurisdictions as well as private organizations have similar and different levels of authority. 2003/0562464

Types of Police Agencies

- Local or municipal police agencies
- Specialized law enforcement agencies
- County police agencies
- County sheriff's departments

Specialized law enforcement agencies have unique duties and in many instances increased police authority for organizations, such as school districts, universities and hospitals as well as transit, port and housing authorities. Many special police agencies can lawfully exercise police authority for a specified distance beyond their primary jurisdiction or on a countywide or statewide basis. School district police officers often have increased authority to investigate private areas on school property without a search warrant.

County police agencies, not to be confused with sheriff's departments, function similarly to local or municipal law enforcement agencies, however their jurisdiction includes all cities within the county.

County sheriff's departments' responsibilities differ on a state-by-state basis. Many sheriff's departments have full enforcement powers across their counties. Deputies may have authority to serve arrest warrants throughout the state, while others are limited to court and jail security duties. In general, sheriff's departments are responsible for holding individuals who have criminal sentences.

Emergency Operations Center (EOC) at the Miami-Dade County Office of Emergency Management. Source: courtesy of Miami-Dade Fire Rescue. 2003/0562474

Local emergency managers build relationships with police, fire, EMS, public health, community volunteer agencies and private sector groups to ensure that they all work well together when responding to a crisis.

Emergency Services at Your Door

Depending on the location, local EMS system may have the resources to provide medical attention in a variety of situations.

- Large, crowded events
- Natural disasters
- Law enforcement incidents
- Water rescue
- Building and wildfires

Local emergency management

The role of emergency management is to help communities prepare, prevent, respond and recover from disasters. Emergency management coordinates all these efforts providing guidance and leadership as needed.

Before an incident
The local emergency management agency helps prepare plans that describe what all first response agencies will do during a crisis. To make this flow as smoothly as possible, the local emergency managers build relationships with police, fire, EMS, public health, community volunteer agencies and private sector groups to ensure that they all work well together while responding to a crisis.

During and after an incident
The local emergency management agency serves as the center of operations during an emergency to monitor, assess damage as well as decide what agencies and resources will be needed. They may activate the county's emergency operations center (EOC) and manage the emergency response effort from this centralized point. Running an EOC includes having representatives from the response agencies and key community leaders, such as the mayor's office and school districts. After an emergency, the local emergency management agency will work with other agencies and organizations to help the community recover from the crisis. They also gather information for decision makers particularly in applying for federal disaster reimbursement funds.

Local emergency medical services (EMS)

Ongoing responsibilities
EMS is made up of emergency medical technicians and paramedics who give immediate medical attention to citizens. They often participate in exercises and planning meetings with public health, hospital, emergency management and other emergency responders to help prepare for major crisis situations. In many communities, EMS personnel train and go out with special law enforcement tactical teams.

During an incident
Depending on the location, the local EMS system may have the resources to provide medical attention in a variety of situations. For incidents at large, crowded events, such as festivals, concerts and sporting events, an ambulance or bike medic teams will respond. Crisis Awareness and Referral in Emergencies (CARE) provide care for victims during large-scale fires, tornados or other emergencies. Disaster medical assistance teams typically go to disaster areas across the country to provide medical support to victims

and to assist the local medical system. Tactical medics provide specialized medical support to law enforcement response teams. Water rescue is available in areas where there are possible victims in the water as well as trapped underwater in vehicles or in flooded buildings. Lastly, wildfire medical and logistical teams care for burn and smoke inhalation victims in addition to other necessary medical treatment.

Local public health agencies

Ongoing responsibilities
Local public health departments and boards of health monitor health issues, food and water safety and supplies as well as offer medical services involving communicable diseases, such as tuberculosis or sexually transmitted diseases. They participate in community health assessments, determine which health issues require the most attention as well as develop and provide health strategies and programs to help reduce health problems. They also monitor and investigate diseases in order to detect and quickly respond to any disease outbreaks or community hazards.

Typical public health programs include:

- Access to primary care among rural and under-served populations for limited types of conditions, such as for young children, family planning or pregnancy
- Promotion of healthy lifestyles
- Injury prevention
- Education and awareness programs to prevent common health problems, such as obesity, sexually transmitted diseases and diabetes

During and after an incident
Public health departments and boards of health fulfill different roles throughout an emergency. After EMS rushes to an incident, teams of doctors and nurses care for the patients. Then, longer-term health care workers, such as physical therapists, social workers, psychiatrists and psychologists, treat ongoing physical and physiological issues.

Response to Anthrax Attacks

"Local public health departments were the first contact for the anthrax cases that occurred in October 2001. They were the primary staff working with the local police and fire departments to investigate many worries about 'white powders.' Local health departments were also the primary source of information to local physicians, hospitals and residents," explains Dr. Susan Allen, Health Director of the Arlington County Department of Human Services in Virginia.

State law enforcement mainly provide public safety on state roadways but also during emergencies. 2003/0562465

State agencies

State emergency response agencies primarily help the local community restore calm after an incident. If disaster strikes and the resources of a community are running low, local emergency response agencies call on state agencies for help.

State law enforcement

Ongoing responsibilities

State law enforcement agencies mainly ensure public safety on state roadways. They patrol their assigned areas, enforce traffic laws, deal with accidents and other emergencies and offer safety programs for the public. Communities and counties that do not have a local police force or a large sheriff's department rely on state troopers for law enforcement services.

During an incident

State law enforcement may be assigned to help local law enforcement agencies maintain order, apprehend and detain suspects, take reports from witnesses, control traffic, process and collect evidence, investigate crime scenes and evacuate areas. State law enforcement agencies frequently provide support in traffic control and direction, tactical response, investigative support, search and rescue operations and riot control.

State EMS

State-level EMS services assist local governments during medical emergencies by supporting local organizations when they need extra help.

Before an incident

Similar to local EMS, but operating on a larger scale, state EMS organizations create and provide procedures to attend to victims' injuries during medical emergencies. They do this through programs that reduce loss of life and damage to the supporting hospitals and health care organizations.

During and after an incident

State EMS services provide resources to save lives and ensure quick medical response to residents. Programs within an EMS system typically include:

- Trauma
- Services for children
- Training and certification for paramedics and emergency medical technicians (EMT)
- Injury prevention

State emergency management agency (EMA)

Every state has some type of EMA. Although its name may differ by state, the functions of a state EMA remain the same.

Ongoing responsibilities
The state EMA will support the planning, response and recovery functions of the local EMA. It will also create statewide emergency planning, prevention and response that includes coordination with other state agencies.

During and after an incident
The state EMA will be busy managing and organizing state organizations and resources as well as providing continuous support to the local EMA. For example, if a citizen reports to the local EMA that a fallen tree is blocking the exit to the neighborhood, the state EMA can send help if the local office is over-taxed. The state EMA also organizes and delivers federal assistance and resources.

State public health

State public health departments provide data collection, technical consultation and support as well as investigate disease outbreaks and enforce public health laws. Because most legal authority for public health is at the state level, they also provide important coordination among localities as well as with other states and federal agencies. State public health services develop and put into place a statewide, connected system of health services prepared for disaster/terrorism incidents, outbreaks of infectious disease and other public health threats and emergencies.

Beyond support to local health offices and local boards of health, state public health roles may include:

- Assessing and researching the health of local communities — except for communicable diseases and environmental hazards
- Detecting and investigating outbreaks of disease (including acts of terrorism)
- Developing and enforcing state health policies
- Preventing diseases and injuries
- Educating the public and health care providers on state and national public health initiatives
- Disseminating health alerts and public health emergencies

Name Game
Names for state emergency management agencies (EMA) vary:

- Civil Defense
- Office of Emergency Services
- Bureau of Disaster Services

State public health departments provide data collection, technical consultation and support as well as investigate disease outbreaks and enforce public health laws.

Stewart Air National Guard Base, Newburgh, NY — New York National Guard 2nd Civil Support Team conducting airload training. They are prepared to deploy anywhere in New York State using its own vehicles and aircraft. Source: Courtesy of NY Army National Guard 2003/0562466

National Guard and Hurricane Andrew

"As Hurricane Andrew bore down on the South Florida coastline in 1996, the Florida National Guard was busy making preparations," recounts a former Army National Guard Intelligence Analyst involved in Hurricane Andrew disaster relief efforts." National Guard Units were pre-positioned at airports at about 70 miles away from areas most vulnerable to the storm. Helicopters, heavy equipment, medical personnel, law enforcement support, patrol, public affairs and civil support teams were organized in the hours before the storm. After the storm had struck a path 40 miles wide, the National Guard sprang into action with helicopters carrying squads charged to restore public order and prevent looting along with medical support personnel. Other Guard members cleared debris from landing zones to make way for the airlift of food, water, medical supplies and electrical generators. Later, this served as a landing area for heavy equipment that cleared the major road leading to the disaster sites. The operation lasted over three months with some Guard Units staying in Miami for up to six months."

National Guard

The National Guard is a branch of the military reserve. The National Guard is also the only branch of the military able to legally bear arms and ammunition by order of the governor, particularly to restore order and prevent looting. Its members are citizens that serve part-time as soldiers. They train on weekends and during the summer. Many members are either military retirees or college students. Increasingly, the National Guard has become a second career for many people who work in medicine, law enforcement and EMS because it provides them with job-related training and experience.

During and after an incident

The National Guard supports police, fire and EMS personnel when they are overwhelmed during a major emergency. Their assistance might include providing food, water, medicine and law enforcement assistance. Because the National Guard has a wide range of heavy equipment — helicopters, amphibious vehicles and heavy trucks — they are often the first to assist after a major disaster. For example, during Hurricane Andrew, when roads were blocked by debris, National Guard helicopters flew into the worst hit areas to provide food, water and medical assistance.

Governor's office

The governor can declare a state of emergency, send out the National Guard and ask the federal government to provide a Presidential Major Disaster Declaration. If you hear officials report that a disaster in your state has been 'a presidential declared disaster', it simply means that the state has exhausted its resources and will receive federal help. In all cases, the governor initiates this process.

Federal agencies

Department of Homeland Security (DHS)

After the attacks on September 11, 2001, the DHS was created by an act of Congress and went into force on March 1, 2003 to help prevent terrorism, respond to major disasters and assist with citizenship services. The DHS responds to governors' requests for assistance in these areas as well. While DHS continues to change and cement its functions, it is currently organized among four major directorates. These four offices seek to centralize resources and responsibilities previously in other federal agencies. Those agencies are in parenthesis for your reference.

Border and Transportation Security

- US Customs Service (Treasury Department)
- Immigration and Naturalization Service (part) (Justice Department)
- Federal Protective Service (General Services Administration (GSA))
- Transportation Security Administration (Transportation Department)
- Federal Law Enforcement Training Center (Treasury Department)
- Animal and Plant Health Inspection Service (part)(Agriculture Department)
- Office for Domestic Preparedness (Justice Department)

Emergency Preparedness and Response

- The Federal Emergency Management Agency (FEMA)
- Strategic National Stockpile and the National Disaster Medical System (Health and Human Services Department)
- Nuclear Incident Response Team (Energy Department)
- Domestic Emergency Support Teams (Justice Department)
- National Domestic Preparedness Office (Federal Bureau of Investigation (FBI), Justice Department)

Science and Technology

- Chemical, Biological, Radiological and Nuclear (CBRN) Countermeasures Programs (Energy Department)
- Environmental Measurements Laboratory (Energy Department)
- National BW Defense Analysis Center (Defense Department)
- Plum Island Animal Disease Center (Agriculture Department)

Information Analysis and Infrastructure Protection

- Critical Infrastructure Assurance Office (Commerce Department)
- Federal Computer Incident Response Center (GSA)
- National Communications System (Defense Department)
- National Infrastructure Protection Center (FBI)
- Energy Security and Assurance Program (Energy Department)

The Secret Service also moved to DHS but will keep the same functions and report directly to the DHS Secretary. the INS adjudications and benefits programs will report directly to the Deputy Secretary as the Bureau of Citizenship and Immigration Services.

US Coast Guard (USCG)

The USCG is a branch of the military but is within DHS. The USCG conducts military, humanitarian and law enforcement functions. USCG responsibilities include: search and rescue, illegal drugs and migrant interdiction, environmental protection as well as maritime security along the US coast line and in ports and waterways.

Department of Homeland Security

The DHS was created to bring together government offices that were previously responsible for preventing terrorism, responding to major disasters and providing citizenship services. DHS departments include:

- Border and Transportation Security
- Emergency Preparedness and Response
- Science and Technology
- Information Analysis and Infrastructure Protection

Yorktown, VA. April 27, 2001 — A US Coast Guard HH-60 Jayhawk helicopter medium-range recovery helicopter that performs search and rescue, law enforcement, military readiness and marine environmental protection missions. Source: photo by PA2 Jacquelyn Zettle, USCG. 2003/0562467

San Juan, Puerto Rico, November 22, 1996 — Metro-Dade (FLTF-1) Task Force began performing search and rescue operations inside the Humberto Vidal Building following a gas mainline explosion. Task force members search for survivors. Source: photo by Bri Rodriguez, FEMA News Photo. 2003/0562468

Global Rescue Teams

Captain Louie Fernandez, Senior Bureau Chief for Miami-Dade Fire Rescue explains, "Over the last several years, Miami-Dade's Urban Search and Rescue Florida Task Force 1 has provided FEMA emergency assistance to the recovery efforts of the Oklahoma City and New York terrorist attacks as well as natural disasters in Turkey, Puerto Rico and throughout South America."

Federal Emergency Management Agency (FEMA)

For the past 24 years, FEMA has been the lead agency organizing the entire federal government to prepare for and respond to national disasters and emergencies declared by the President. Approximately 26 other federal agencies have signed on with FEMA to provide help under the Federal Response Plan which describes how groups within the federal government cooperate during disasters. Examples of these agencies and departments include:

- Environmental Protection Agency (EPA)
- Department of Health and Human Services (HHS)/Public Health Service/The Centers for Disease Control and Prevention (CDC)
- Department of Energy (DOE)
- Department of Defense (DOD) (several divisions, including the US Army Corps of Engineers)
- Department of Transportation (DOT)
- Small Business Administration (SBA)

The SBA provides very low interest disaster loans to help the victims of a tragedy recover financially and contributes a significant amount of aid. See *Chapter 10: After an Emergency: What do I do Now?* for instructions on applying for disaster loans through FEMA as the umbrella agency.

FEMA urban search and rescue teams

Currently FEMA has 28 Urban Search and Rescue (USAR) teams established in the continental United States that are completely drawn from local emergency responders. Through formal agreements with FEMA, local USAR teams receive equipment and training as part of a nationwide disaster response plan. When not called into service for the federal government, these responders are the same people who provide local services, such as search and rescue, fire, police or EMS.

Federal Bureau of Investigation (FBI)

The Federal Bureau of Investigation (FBI) is an office of the Department of Justice responsible for investigating and tracking a wide range of crime that crosses state, national and international boundaries. The FBI is also a part of the ongoing effort to protect US citizens from acts of terrorism. The following are FBI prevention and response priorities:

- Terrorist attacks
- Foreign intelligence operations and espionage
- Cyber-based attacks and high tech crimes
- Public corruption at all levels
- Breach of civil rights
- Transnational and national criminal organizations
- Major white collar crime

- Significant violent crime
- Support for federal, state, local and international partners

In addition, the FBI will provide investigative and law enforcement support resources to local and state agencies in the event of catastrophic crime or acts of terrorism. For example, in the DC sniper shootings of October 2002, the FBI provided investigators and counter-sniper resources to aid the efforts of local law enforcement.

How local, state and federal agencies work together

Many times, different agencies and organizations respond together to provide specific roles and responsibilities. Whether these groups are dealing with a natural disaster, accident or terrorist event, their responses will essentially be the same. State, county or local emergency operations plans describe the actions of each agency along with how they coordinate with other organizations. The agencies and organizations will likely do the following to deal with a disaster:

Many times, different agencies and organizations respond together to provide specific roles and responsibilities.

- Assess the situation.
- Save lives and attend to injured.
- Preserve property.
- Minimize the damage.
- Call in extra help, if needed.
- Recover from the incident (emotionally and physically).

Local agencies are the first to arrive and respond to an emergency. If they need additional help, they request resources from state response agencies. Volunteer organizations may help at this time as well. Once these groups respond and assess the damage, the governor may deploy the National Guard, make a Major Disaster Declaration, commit state funds for recovery and/or request for federal funds. The Federal Emergency Management Agency (FEMA) will review the governor's request and recommend action to the White House for the President to decide if the incident requires a Presidential Major Disaster Declaration. The following flow chart diagram 2.1 shows how groups work together to respond to a disaster.

Emmitsburg, MD, March 10, 2003 — An Incident Command System (ICS) course is held at FEMA's National Emergency Training Center, one of dozens of courses offered there each year for first responders, emergency managers and educators. Source: photo by Jocelyn Augustino, FEMA News Photo. 2003/0562470

Incident Command System

During an incident, response agencies work together using ICS. This system defines who is in charge, creates a team process for decision-making as well as develops ways to collect and share information.

Diagram 2.1 Interagency Response Flow Chart

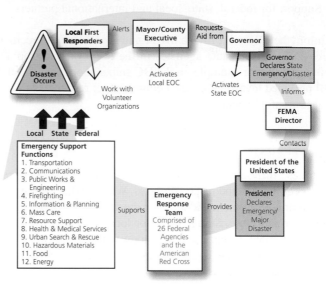

Emergency response cooperation

Response agencies must work together in many ways to manage a disaster effectively. One of the more effective ways in which agencies work together is through the Incident Command System (ICS) that defines who is in charge, creates a team process for decision-making as well as develops ways to collect and share information internally and to the public. Accomplishing this means that five areas must work together: command, operations, planning, logistics as well as finance and administration.

Understanding ICS will be helpful to you if you are seeking help or volunteering your services during an emergency. Doing so will help you avoid wasting valuable time requesting assistance from the wrong agency. This system will most likely be run through your local EOC.

Health care cooperation

It is extremely important that all health care organizations work together during an emergency so that anyone with a medical emergency can call 911 or a local emergency services number and receive a quick medical response. To do so, EMS, hospitals and public health agencies plan with state and local health departments, hospitals and other health care organizations to cooperate. For example, public health departments would play the main role in a public health emergency requiring mass distribution of vaccine or antibiotics. Hospitals and other health care organizations would take care of casualties.

Public information

An agency's communications staff, usually known as the public affairs or media relations department, and private media organizations play very important roles in informing and directing citizens before, during and after emergencies. Public safety depends on the ability of responders as well as spokespersons to inform, calm and listen to the public.

Role of public affairs

All organizations, especially public agencies, must speak and listen to the public efficiently and quickly on a regular basis. Different public agencies and their senior leaders have different views about using the media to communicate with the public. Public agencies do, however, have legal obligations under freedom of information laws to let the public know certain information. Public agencies must follow rules on releasing certain types of information affecting operations, security, investigations and victims and their families. You request public information in different ways: media inquiries, formal petitions for documents, individual or organization letters of inquiry or phone calls to lawmakers and officials.

Before an incident

Public affairs departments have staff trained and experienced in operations such as fire rescue, law enforcement or paramedics as well as journalism or public relations. Sometimes these departments are made up of just one person known most often as a public information officer (PIO) working full- or part-time. In some ways, PIOs serve as inside reporters; they gather the facts from the scene and explain the situation and any instructions to the public. Because these teams need time to gather information and organize press conferences and interviews, news usually arrives in bursts.

During an incident

At the beginning of most emergencies, the scene is chaotic and information is incomplete and even conflicting. In most cases, a disaster information center will be set up to provide the public accurate and updated information. To maintain order during a disaster, emergency response agencies centralize their public affairs officers to provide an organized source of information to the public, their partner organizations, government officials and area businesses through the media.

To receive as much information when disasters have longer-term effects, watch for press conferences and interviews as well as hotline numbers, public meetings and open letters to the public in the newspaper and mailings. If you have access to the Internet, the web sites of emergency response agencies also provide useful updates, background information and ways to seek and give help.

Role of Public Information

"Our emergency public information efforts have much more influence over operational outcomes than many of us likes to admit. Not only does news coverage inevitably feed back (hopefully not too much) into our command centers, [but] it also shapes the perspectives and expectations of responders and citizens alike," says Art Botterell, Principal of the emergency management Internet company Incident.com and former staff member of the California Office of Emergency Services and FEMA.

Source: *Jane's Crisis Communications Handbook (2003)*

At the beginning of most emergencies, the scene is chaotic and information is incomplete and even conflicting.

Miami-Dade, Firefighter and Urban Search and Rescue K-9 handler Hilda Wood and Senior Bureau Chief, Public Affairs Chief Louie Fernandez talk to the media. Source: Courtesy of Miami-Dade Fire Rescue. 2003/0562472

Media Alerts

Severe flooding in the state of Georgia resulted in poisonous snakes relocating. The media was used to informing the public about the possibility that the snakes might turn up in new, unexpected areas.

Media role in emergencies

Disasters are a significant source of news and the media play an important role in informing the public as quickly and as accurately as possible. The media are essential in covering an event for the public as well as the responders and other government officials. Because citizens receive most of their information through the press, the media also influence public perception on local, national and global levels.

During an incident

During a disaster, pay close attention to information on the radio, television and in the newspapers. Updates, instructions and information hotline numbers are just a few kinds of information that may be announced.

Look for the following types of news to protect yourself during an incident:

- Event news and updates
- Type of event
- Event location and the area(s) affected and to avoid
- Evacuation routes
- Weather: approaching storms, flooded areas, areas to avoid

Public services

- Emergency resources: shelter (for people and pets), food, water, medical care, multi-lingual services
- Information hotline numbers

Self-protection guidance

- Ways to protect yourself during and after the emergency at home, work, school and/or in the community

Keep in mind, however, that the media have helicopters, cherry pickers, boats and other ways to be close to a situation and that they may arrive before the responders. They start reporting before the responders have time to collect and provide information. As a result, information arrives in bits and pieces and may not always be accurate given the confusion that surrounds emergencies. If time permits, listen to the advice of the authorities before taking decisive action.

Change in media coverage of security

Since the attacks of September 11, 2001, continuing threats to safety and security have heightened press interest and public desire for related information. Consequently, the media often present a security incident as possibly terrorism-related until it is proven to be otherwise. For instance, when authorities suspected a chemical-biological threat in Miami

International Airport on August 21, 2002, the local, national and international media sent a flurry of inquiries to the Miami-Dade Fire Rescue Public Affairs Office within five minutes of the response dispatch. In the end, however, the incident was not terrorism as speculated or serious.

Although the media now reacts more quickly to any news related to possible security threats, their limited resources and desire to report exclusive stories also shift their attention to the next big incident more quickly. In other words, the media devote more resources to a particular story but for a shorter amount of time. For example, the TWA Flight 800 crash off the coast of New York in 1996 caused 230 fatalities and attracted over 600 members of the press for over 30 days. In contrast, the media coverage of American Airlines Flight 587 crash in Queens, New York, on November 12, 2001, caused more casualties, had a similar potential terrorist cause and was located close to the same large New York area media market. Media attention, however, lasted for only about three days.

The expansion of the Internet, cable television and wireless communications provides information to the public more quickly and also creates a greater need for media outlets to break exclusive stories.

Stories that make the news

Whether a story is deemed newsworthy often depends on the presence, or absence, of other significant news. For example, on a slow news day a workplace-violence incident may attract national coverage, whereas on a busy news day only local media outlets would cover the incident. Several types of crises generally attract media attention. Incidents affecting many people, especially on local but also on national and/or international levels:

- Major public safety incidents
- Terrorism
- Mass casualties
- War or large-scale conflicts
- Violence involving children
- Natural disasters
- Incompetence or wrongdoing of a government agency or a corporation
- Dangerous commercial products
- Incidents of public outrage and civil disturbance
- Criminal investigations or trials with significant legal or social impact
- Local stories that affect others outside the community
- Events that yield unexpected, shocking, bizarre, exotic details/images
- Human interest stories, such as the rescue of a small child or animal
- Stories with celebrity involvement
- Stories deemed to be of public interest by news ratings

Disasters attract local, national and international media to report the progress of the response and announce key public information.
2003/0564529

Media Relations in Action

LTC Robert Domenici, then Commander of the National Guard Weapons of Mass Destruction Civil Response Unit responsible for counter-terrorism, recalls the cooperation he experienced with the media on September 11, 2001:

"The media was on hand in force and knew the Civil Support Team was tied up in several sensitive operations [at Ground Zero]. The media wanted interviews and information on operations. Because we had trained with the media on hand prior and conducted interviews in the past, they knew our mission and the sensitivity of its nature. They worked out a time and place for interviews by holding meetings with the different sections. The media played a vastly different role by gathering this information and disseminating it back for the other sections to use in their operations. The media acted as a conduit and assistor in the information flow."

Source: *Jane's Crisis Communications Handbook (2003)*

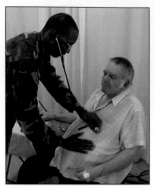

Houston, Texas June 19 2001 — The 59th Medical wing from Lackland, Texas, treat patients at the mobile medical unit set up at the Astrodome in Houston after Tropical Storm Allison. Source: photo by Andrea Booher, FEMA News Photo. 2003/0564545

Major emergencies that cause many people to become sick or injured may require hospitals to organize alternative care facilities.

Other local resources

There are many organizations in your community that provide a major or supporting role in disaster response and recovery. Some of these roles vary from community to community. No matter how small or large their role may be, find out their responsibilities to help you during a disaster so that you know what to expect.

Hospitals

Major emergencies that cause many people to become sick or injured may require hospitals to organize alternative care facilities. Listen to local news and emergency bulletins or call the hospital information line to find out where alternative care facilities are located.

Follow the instructions of health care officials during an emergency.

- If you are given medications in a mass medication distribution, make sure you read and understand the directions and possible side effects.
- Maintain correct and updated health information for everyone in your family.
- Do not call the hospital to ask about general information on the disaster; ask only urgent health-related questions.
- Always inform health care officials of any pre-existing medical condition you may have as well as any allergies and current medications.

Transportation: public works sector

During an incident

The local and state transportation authorities will work around the clock during a crisis to keep roads clear and support the evacuations. Their primary disaster functions include:

- Evacuate people whose lives are endangered.
- Provide effective and coordinated response to actual or potential disasters that make using highways and roads difficult.
- Help in emergency debris removal.
- Direct traffic rerouting and assist police agencies at the site.
- Provide equipment, flashing lights, warning lights, cones, signs or other traffic control devices.

Transportation organizations will help with evacuations but they will not help you move back into your home. Many people request this service, but local transportation authority cannot tie up valuable disaster resources for such individual services.

Transportation authorities have to prioritize their resources and depending on the nature of the disaster, road repair needs may not be addressed immediately.

Typically transportation priority will be given to:

- Maintenance repairs of an urgent nature to keep open access to critical infrastructure, such as hospitals or emergency response agencies
- Road restoration for heavy, high-speed traffic routes
- Debris cleanup of non-cargo items only after authorities declare the area safe

Houston, TX, June 23, 2001 — Debris removal trucks lined up to dump yards of debris at a landfill, following Tropical Storm Allison. Transportation authorities must prioritize their resources to clean up a disaster area. Source: photo by Andrea Booher, FEMA Photo News. 2003/0562453

American Red Cross (ARC)

If you cannot access roads and need emergency transportation, you should call emergency services immediately and explain your situation. If your situation is not an immediate emergency, but you have a critical need for transportation, the ARC can provide emergency transportation. In addition, the ARC will provide other emergency relief services, such as food distribution and home repair assistance. These services are provided for individuals, communities, states and countries worldwide. If you are in need of ARC assistance or wish to find out more about how to obtain disaster relief contact your local ARC chapter or go to www.redcross.org.

If you are in need of ARC assistance or wish to find out more about how to obtain disaster relief contact your local ARC chapter or go to www.redcross.org.

Training and volunteering

A number of organizations provide disaster response training to civilians and community response teams. The American Red Cross, local emergency management, local public safety agencies (police, fire, rescue), Department of Justice and the Citizen Corps are just a few organizations that provide training for citizens to prepare themselves and help in the event of a disaster.

Sources of emergency training information

The following organizations provide emergency preparedness and response training brochures and booklets:

- Department of Homeland Security
- American Red Cross
- American Red Cross' Safety Tips for People with Disabilities
- Federal Emergency Management Agency (FEMA) Preparedness Information
- FEMA Safety Rules for Kids

Sterling, VA., March 7, 2001 — Community members review information about the Citizens Corps Neighborhood Watch program after a community meeting. Source: photo by Elise Moore, FEMA News Photo. 2003/0562471

- Centers for Disease Control and Prevention
- National Weather Service (NWS) Preparedness and Safety Information
- The Weather Channel
- National Severe Storms Laboratory
- National Oceanic and Atmospheric Administration (NOAA) Safety Tips — Weather and Natural Disaster Related
- NOAA Education Weather for Kids and Students

Citizen Corps

Citizen Corps is a component of the USA Freedom Corps — a White House initiative to increase volunteerism supporting domestic security efforts. Coordinated by FEMA, Citizen Corps is made up of concerned citizens who are trained to respond to any emergency situation. Citizen Corps seeks to enhance preparedness, training and citizen involvement in order to support first responders. To learn more about your local Citizen Corps initiatives, contact your local emergency management agency or go to www.citizencorps.gov. The following groups are sub-sets of Citizen Corps.

Medical Reserve Corps

Medical Reserve Corps units are community-based and made up of health care professionals who provide volunteer services in their communities for emergencies and ongoing public health services. Medical Reserve Corps members help with a wide array of emergencies, such as an influenza epidemic, a chemical spill or an act of terrorism. The Medical Reserve Corps may provide direct support to medical first responders during emergencies and will ride with them on emergency calls.

Volunteers in Police Services (VIPS)

VIPS allows sworn police officers to volunteer time patrolling the streets. Volunteers are assigned to local law enforcement agencies. During a disaster you can ask your local VIPS representative for information about the disaster as well as support for you and your family.

Community Emergency Response Teams (CERT)

The CERT program provides citizens with emergency response training. During an emergency, you can rely on CERT members to provide immediate assistance to you and your community. They can also help the community with non-emergency safety projects that help improve safety.

USA on Watch

USA on Watch is part of the National Association Neighborhood Watch Program. The Neighborhood Watch Program has given Americans a unique way to protect their communities by working together with local officials, law enforcement and other citizens. This program makes citizens an active part of preventing crime. If your local community has a Neighborhood Watch Program, refer them to *Chapter 7: Staying Alert and Reporting Incidents.*

Private town hall style meetings

Town hall style meetings conducted by private consultants can also help you learn how to prevent and respond to disasters. These individuals, however, may not be licensed professionals education or public safety. As a result, the quality of their experience, advice and approach may vary widely. When seeking training, use as many sources of information as possible, such as the government, private experts, the media and other resources.

Quiz yourself, family and friends

1. What is the role of law enforcement during an emergency?

2. How do local, state and federal response agencies work together during an incident?

3. In the event that a large number of people need emergency medical treatment and the local hospitals run out of beds, what is most likely to happen?

   A. The hospitals will stop admitting people needing assistance.
   B. Victims are airlifted to a nearby community hospital.
   C. People will be expected to treat each other at home.
   D. Alternate care facilities will be set up in your community.

4. What does the media provide during an emergency?

5. Where can you find volunteer opportunities?

Find out the answers to the Chapter 2 quiz on page 200.

Part 2
Preparation

Take steps to prepare for emergencies and prevent damage. Source: photo by Dave Gatley, FEMA News Photo. 2003/0562480

Part Two **Chapter 3**

Personal Disaster Preparedness

"Call it pre-traumatic stress disorder. For people who spend a lot of time in Washington and watch too much TV, the anxiety level can be as high as the threat level. Once you could count me among them. No more," said Sally Quinn. *"Now I'm prepared and I'm the calmest person I know,"* she concluded.

Life seems dangerous indeed, but people today have more resources than ever to address their worries.

"Ready…"

by Sally Quinn, *Washington Post*, Sunday, March 16, 2003

Introduction

Being organized in your personal affairs reduces stress and better prepares you for daily life. Understanding and preparing for the risks in your community may put you more at ease as for Sally Quinn.

Emergencies such as fires, hazardous materials spills, power outages or natural disasters can happen in almost any place at almost any time. If disaster strikes, you need to be ready to take care of yourself and your family. Local officials and relief workers will do everything they can to respond quickly, but they cannot reach everyone right away. **Emergency services professionals recommend that citizens prepare to take care of themselves for the first 72 hours after a disaster.**

Understanding stress

This chapter specifically starts with understanding stress because planning for a disaster can bring up stressful and negative thoughts. Stress is the pressure we experience mentally and physically in response to both positive and negative events in our lives. It is 'emotional aftershock' that occurs

Chapter Overview

This chapter discusses how to prepare a disaster plan and emergency supplies.

- Handling stress
- Family disaster planning
- Home preparation
- Emergency go-kit supplies: home, medical and car
- Personal affairs
- Considerations for firearm owners
- Training and volunteering

when something overwhelming happens to you. Losing your job may be a negative stress, whereas moving to your dream city may be a positive, yet stressful event. Responding to these stresses is a reality that we deal with everyday and understanding how to cope with them is critical to your physical and emotional health.

Stress and emergencies

Whether you were directly involved or saw footage on television, it is important to know that each person reacts differently to disasters. It is both normal and expected for a person to experience a range of responses following a traumatic experience. Traumatic stress changes the way adults and children experience the world. They may no longer see the world as a safe place nor will they trust the people in it in quite the same way. These reactions may affect your physical health, disposition and even performance at work. In many cases, families lash out at each other after disasters with increases in domestic violence as one indicator. Post-Traumatic Stress Disorder (PTSD) is another emotional response of feeling fearful after the event. PTSD can happen immediately or sometimes months after the incident.

How can I plan to deal with stress?

There are different options to help you deal with stress from daily life and a disaster. Maintaining a healthy lifestyle will make you less susceptible to the effects of stress. Regularly exercising and eating healthy foods is a good way to prevent or manage it. If you are involved in stressful activities on a day-to-day basis, it is important to break your routine and shift your focus away from the stressful activity. For more information on the symptoms, effects and treatment for stress after an emergency, see *Chapter 11: Psychological Effects of an Emergency*.

Disaster preparedness

To create a plan to prevent, respond and recover from a variety of potential emergencies, use the outline *Eight-step Plan to Emergency Preparedness* in *Chapter 1: Why Should I Use This Planning Guide?* on page 8.

Risks in your community

Think about the different kinds of emergencies that could happen in your community to start your planning. Do you live near an interstate, port or major rail line by which hazardous materials are transported? Do you live near a factory or nuclear power plant? Are you in an area that sometimes floods? For each possible emergency, begin putting together plans to help keep your family safe should such emergencies occur. If you are unsure what types of events affect your community, talk to your local emergency management officials. They know what types of area hazards you should include in your preparedness planning.

Evacuation plans

Plan ahead and determine the best escape routes out of your home and neighborhood. If possible, find two ways out of each room. The following are recommended precautions to take when evacuating:

Look around your community to know the areas vulnerable to emergencies, such as high water passes. 2003/0562493

- Listen to a battery-powered radio or car radio and follow the instructions of local emergency officials. **Do not use shortcuts because certain areas may be impassable or dangerous.**
- Take your emergency/disaster supplies kit with you.
- Wear protective clothing and sturdy shoes.
- If you do not own a vehicle or drive, learn in advance what your community's arrangements are for those without private transportation.

Seeking shelter

Many times, emergencies simply require you to remain in your home or elsewhere safely indoors. This is referred to as 'shelter-in-place.' In the event you cannot shelter at home, find out where designated shelters are located in your community through the local emergency management or mayor's office. If you have pets, look into which facilities accept them and other options for their care, such as hotels and kennel rentals.

Make sure everyone in your family knows the evacuation plan and that you have supplies ready to take with you. 2003/0562475

Because different disasters require sheltering-in-place in different areas of a building, look for specific guidance on likely hazards in *Chapter 8: Natural Disasters & Accidents* or *Chapter 9: Hazardous Materials and Weapons of Mass Destruction*. For example, going underground during a tornado can save your life but doing so during a chemical spill could bring you closer to the danger because some chemicals settle to the ground. During a flood, it is best to shelter as far above ground as possible. If you chose, you can also create a safe room in your home for sheltering-in-place. See page 41 for information on creating a safe room.

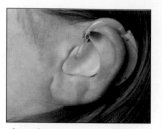

If you have special needs, such as hearing problems, make sure you have back-up equipment ready for an emergency.
2003/0562477

Horsham, PA June 20, 2001 — Red Cross worker Jeff Brodeur aids deaf flood victim at the service center. Source: photo by Liz Roll, FEMA News Photo.
2003/0562476

Develop a family communication plan for everyone to know how and where to reconnect if the family is separated.

Special needs: children, elderly and disabled

The term special needs refers not only to people with disabilities but also to any unique situation that needs additional planning or poses exceptional challenges. Depending on your situation, you may need to make special arrangements for your disaster plan.

Whether you care for children, elderly or disabled people, be sure you have a plan for the following in your community and your home:

- Safe evacuation and shelter-in-place options
- Food and water for specific dietary needs
- Medical assistance with machines, devices or medicine
- Transportation

Communication plans

Discuss with your family, close friends and neighbors how to communicate during a disaster. If you know the people in your community and neighborhood, it will be easier to work together if an emergency were to occur. Such discussions can help reduce fear and anxiety during an emergency.

Family communications

Because most families are rarely together during a typical day, you should create an emergency communication plan that can go into affect when children are at school and adults are at work. Your communication plan should include when and how you will communicate with each other. Fill out important numbers in the cut out cards in *Chapter 12: Appendices* and keep it in your emergency go-kit and with you at all times.

Leaving messages

In the event of an emergency, decide together the key information everyone needs to communicate. This can be the following information which can also include specific needs, such as if a family member or friend needs medication or to be picked up.

- Your well being
- Your current location
- Where you will meet and estimated time of arrival

Important numbers

Make sure everyone has access to key numbers to use during an emergency:

- Work number(s): family members and neighbor

- Your child's school/university
- Out-of-town family contact person
- Local public safety agencies: fire, police, emergency medical services (EMS), local hospital

How to contact each other
Establishing one central place for all the members of your family to check in can prevent confusion and panic. After a disaster, it is often easier to call long distance; therefore, plan to contact an out-of-town relative or friend as the central family contact person, particularly if evacuation is necessary.

There are a variety of ways people can contact each other depending on the types of communications resources you use and the situation:

- Call telephone/pager contact numbers of family members.
- Leave a message at a central home answering machine or voice mail that everyone can access using a pass code.
- Send an email to a family, friends or co-worker list.
- Broadcast on a shortwave/HAM radio, if licensed.
- Leave a note on the front door, the car or at your place of work.

Make sure everyone in the family knows how to reach one central family contact person in the event of an emergency or separation. 2003/0562478

Make sure that you have adequate equipment to communicate with your family in an emergency because during an incident, communications networks are easily overwhelmed. Even if you have the latest and greatest equipment, network connections can be strained. Therefore, have a back-up to every method of communication in your disaster plan. For every phone you use, have a way to back it up in case the (cell) phones do not work. Some cities and states now have priority usage agreements for cell phone use that means emergency responders may have first access to available phone lines. Check with your local emergency management office to find out if your community uses these agreements.

For every phone you use, have a way to back it up in case the (cell) phones do not work.

Meeting places
Pick two places to meet during or after an emergency. The first meeting place should be a location right outside of your home, such as in the case of a home fire. The second location should be a place away from your neighborhood in case you can't return home, such as with an evacuation.

Families should establish two emergency meeting places: one near home and one away from the neighborhood in case of an evacuation.

Preparing with neighbors and the community

Preparing for a community emergency is a responsibility that begins with each individual. If you band together with the community, you can face disasters as a unit and recover as a community. If you coordinate your

Talk to your neighbors about working together during and after an emergency. 2003/0562479

FEMA Hazard Mitigation. Moving a water heater above ground level will help save the appliance and keep it working during a flood. Source: photo by Dave Gatley, FEMA News Photo. 2003/0562480

Safety Resources

The **Institute for Business and Home Safety (IBHS),** provides tips for regular safety check-ups that you can order from IBHS 4775 E. Fowler Avenue Tampa, FL 33617, E-mail: info@ibhs.org or Tel: 1-813- 286-3400.

The **American Red Cross (ARC) Health and Safety Tips** is also a good source available online at www.redcross.org/ services/hss/index.html or by calling your local ARC chapter.

procedures with your neighbors and community response agencies, you'll find that more heads are indeed better than one. This needs to be a strong effort because many people hardly know their neighbors, particularly in urban areas.

Community and business meetings

Many community and business meetings focus on special topics including disaster preparedness that will give you insight into the efforts of the community and local businesses. You will also meet people who can help you in your planning. Look for opportunities at community meetings to learn preparedness as well as give your ideas, such as the following:

- Learn about the hazards within your community.
- Understand the roles and responsibilities of your local government officials and business leaders.
- Provide input about your neighborhood during safety talks.
- Educate others on specific issues that you have encountered in your experience with emergencies or with your disaster preparedness.

Home preparedness

Once you identify the risks to your home and community, consider how to prepare your home to reduce the likelihood and impact of potential danger. There are general ways to make your home safer as well as in terms of specific incidents. See *Chapter 8: Natural Disasters & Accidents* and *Chapter 9: Hazardous Materials and Weapons of Mass Destruction* for ways to prepare your home for incidents that are likely to occur in your area.

General home safety considerations

Taking a few simple steps can make your home safer on a daily basis.

- **Throw rugs** need anti-skid bottoms. Often people lay these rugs at the foot of a stairway. Children or adults in a hurry will run down the stairway and fall, causing sprains and broken bones.
- **Bathtubs** need anti-slip mats. People often forget to ensure they have anti-slip mats installed or simply forget that a wet smooth surface is a dangerous.
- **Back-up generators** must be grounded or have an electrician install a back surge protector.
- **Pools** need to be secured with fencing so that small children or pets do not climb into a pool unattended and hurt themselves. Pools are another place where people can easily slip and fall.
- **Air ducts:** dust particles can build up in y our home including the air ducts to extent of affecting the ventilation capacity and air quality. Consider having the air ducts professionally cleaned every few years.

▪ **Mold:** exist in over 3,000 varieties in homes with a history of water damage and are a serious and unrecognized allergic problem for many adults and children. Homes and apartments with these molds can cause a variety of health problems forcing citizens to permanently vacate their homes. Related health problems are also difficult for doctors to diagnose. Some molds will **permanently contaminate** all of your belongings: clothes, furniture and even electronics. Insurance companies do not cover related doctor bills, your possessions or home reconstruction. No environmental laws exist to offer any legal recourse. For information on the symptoms and your options, see the Center for Disease Control and Prevention at www.cdc.gov or (Tel.) 1-800-311-3435; or the non-profit organization Mold Across America at www.moldacrossamerica.org, (Tel.) 1-877-280-MOLD (East coast) or (Tel.) 1-866-810-MOLD (West coast).

Exposed wires outside of your home should be secured and protected from the weather.
2003/0562487

Safe rooms

Having a safe room does not have to involve building an addition or renting an extra room. It can simply involve deciding what rooms and locations are the safest for possible emergencies. These rooms may serve as the sole protection for your family and neighbors in the event of certain kinds of emergencies. During tornados it is important to seek shelter below ground (in a basement) or in a windowless, reinforced room on the first floor in the center of your home, such as a bathroom. Consider preparing safe rooms in your house or identifying potential ones in your apartment building to shelter-in-place if you need to stay home during a disaster.

If you want to create a safe a room in your home, consider reinforcing one room by fortifying the walls, ceiling, door and even flooring to withstand extreme winds and flying debris. Protection against other hazards, such as home invasions, are available as well but can sometimes provide an illusion of security when the best course of action may be to escape to a neighbor's home.

Sealed rooms

There has been much said about the US Department of Homeland Security's advice to prepare a sealed room in your home in the case of a chemical or biological incident. Opinions on the usefulness of sealed rooms vary from person to person. As discussed in *Chapter 9: Hazardous Materials and Weapons of Mass Destruction*, a variety of uncontrollable weather conditions have to be just right to allow chemical and biological releases to be harmful. If a large scale chemical release occurred near your home, such

Safe Room Resources

The **Federal Emergency Management Agency (FEMA)** provides instructions on hardening a room in your home on a CD-Rom and in hard copy. Request a mailed copy by calling FEMA at 1-800-480-2520 and ask for FEMA 388-CD.

The **Wind Engineering Research Center** at Texas Tech University also provides technical guidance about home shelters. Their toll free number is 1-(888) 946-3287, ext. 336.

Use Safe Rooms Selectively

LTC Robert Domenici who was Commander of the National Guard WMD Civil Response Team in New York City on September 11, 2001 recounts: "In many of the buildings surrounding The World Trade Center, the NYC EOC [Emergency Operations Center] evacuated personnel to the basement. As a result, when The World Trade Center Tower collapsed, they almost buried the Mayor along with his city management team. A janitor led them to safety through a ground floor exit. This is an important lesson. The basement is not the safest room for all emergencies and sometimes it is better to evacuate than to seek shelter."

as with a train derailment releasing a toxic amount of chemicals, the authorities most likely will tell you to stay in the highest level of your house or apartment building with the windows shut and the ventilation system off until further notice. If the area affected is large, after the chemicals settle the authorities would give evacuation instructions while helping those in the most danger with special equipment. In this situation, you could enter a room without windows, such as the bathroom, and cover openings with towels or go into a sealed room already prepared.

If you decide a sealed room is the best way to ensure your safety, understand how to use it and that it is effective for only a short amount of time.

- Go to an interior room without windows and above ground level. (Some chemicals are heavier than air and may seep into basements.)
- Using duct tape, seal all cracks around the door and any vents into the room. Include spaces around pipes.

How to use sealed rooms effectively

If you shelter-in-place or seek shelter in a prepared sealed room and decide to remain there for TEMPORARY protection, take note of key factors upon entering. If possible, contact emergency services (EMS) and give them this information:

- Your location
- Air supply
- Number of people
- Time you entered and sealed the entrance
- Time the seal must be broken to prevent suffocation
- If oxygen bottles or air filters are available, make note of how much additional time this allows.

If possible, stay abreast of emergency updates and information by radio, television or by phone.

How long can I stay in a sealed room?

Leave the sealed room before oxygen and carbon dioxide levels become dangerous. Generally, one person has 2 minutes worth of air per cubic foot of space in a room.

Sealed Room Air Supply Formula

$\dfrac{2 \times \text{length} \times \text{width} \times \text{height of room (in feet)}}{\text{number of people in the room}}$ = Safe time limit (in minutes)

Example: calculating safe time limit
One room 10 feet wide, 10 feet long and 8 feet high

One person would have about 26 hours and 40 minutes of safe air.
Two people in the same room would have about 13 hours and 20 minutes.
Three people would have approximately 8 hours and 52 minutes.

People **generally would need to stay in a sealed room from one to 10 hours to avoid contamination;** although, all incidents are different depending on the amount and delivery of the release, weather conditions as well as surrounding buildings and terrain. If possible, listen for an 'all clear' announcement from first responders and exit.

Emergency Supplies

In the event of a disaster, have emergency supplies on hand to take care of yourself and your family until responders reach you or you reach a location to receive assistance. As you begin planning, think about how long you may be without vital services. These services can include: electricity, water, gas, emergency medical assistance, fire services, law enforcement, transportation, telecommunications, television and even radio.

Emergency 'go-kits'
Emergency 'go-kits' hold supplies that you will need to use in the event of an emergency or an evacuation from your home. You should have an emergency 'go-kit' stocked and available well ahead of time. The essentials you will need to survive for the short-term are water, vital medicines and shelter. Everything else is really a luxury. That isn't to say there aren't significant advantages to having food and first aid supplies but they come second after the most basic essentials. If you must prioritize what to gather, first, stock water, then food and first aid supplies and then other necessities.

Home supplies
The following are common items to include in a 'go-kit' to assist you and your family during and after a disaster. These items are also listed in cut-out forms in *Chapter 12: Appendices.* Keep a few things in mind while preparing your home emergency 'go-kit.' Have enough supplies in your home to meet the needs of each family member for at least three days. Assemble an emergency supplies kit with items you may need if asked to evacuate. Store the kit in a sturdy, easy-to-carry container, such as a backpack, duffel bag or plastic storage bin. Once your kit is assembled, do not forget regular maintenance. Ask one person to be responsible for replacing water every three months, food every six months and batteries on a yearly basis.

People used to keep pantries full of non-perishable foods before convenience stores and 24-hour supermarkets existed. 2003/0562481

Back in the Day

"In the 1950s, before convenience stores were common, most families had cupboards full of tins and dried goods," recounts Roger Davies, a former British military officer with counter-terrorism experience in Northern Ireland. "These days most people barely keep a day's supply. In addition, the vulnerability of modern just-in-time delivery systems to the logistical infrastructure of food markets is crucial. Most supermarkets today do not have a warehouse, and the food goes straight off the back of a truck onto the shelves. Britain became aware of this when there was a fuel truckers' strike a couple of years ago. Within three days there was no fuel, so no supermarkets were re-supplied. Two days later the shelves were empty. Going back to simple planning and saving for a stocked pantry will allow you to avoid shortages and spending more on scarce items than otherwise necessary."

Pack a go-kit with emergency supplies and involve your children in the process.
2003/0562482

Organize first aid supplies in the event stores are closed or if you have to evacuate.
2003/0562483

The money you spend on home safety tools, such as fire extinguishers, is worth your life and home. 2003/0562486

Food and water

- At least one week of non-perishable, high protein food
- Three-to five-day supply of water (one gallon per person per day)
- A manual can opener
- Food and water for your pets

Clothing and personal items

- One change of clothing and footwear and one blanket or sleeping bag per person
- Contacts or an extra pair of glasses, if necessary
- A credit card and cash (small denominations) or travelers checks
- Recent photos of family members for identification
- Important family documents in a waterproof container. (Keep the originals of important financial and family documents in a safe place. You will need accessible records for tax and insurance purposes.)
- Special items for infant, elderly or disabled family members

First aid and sanitary items

- Sanitation supplies: toilet paper and paper towels, soap, plastic garbage bags and disinfectant
- Toiletries: toothbrushes, toothpaste, razors, deodorant, feminine products, diapers
- Basic first-aid kit: extra refill of prescriptions, medication, multi-vitamins, bandages and appropriate tape, antiseptic, thermometer, tweezers, scissors, latex gloves, betadine, hydrogen peroxide and alcohol, anti-bacterial ointment, anti-bacterial soap that does not require water, instant hot/cold packs

Tools

- Battery-powered radio
- Flashlights
- Extra batteries
- Waterproof matches and waterproof lighters are essential items.
- Multi-purpose tool (knife, tweezers, bottle opener)
- Wrench and instructions to turn off utilities, such as gas and water
- Plastic bucket with tight lid
- Work gloves
- Note pad, pen and paper
- Multi-purpose duct tape
- Plastic sheeting
- A tent in the event of evacuation
- Fire extinguisher (ABC type) (Be sure everyone knows how to use and find it.)
- An emergency guide, such as a first aid book/chart

Medical needs

Pre-existing conditions

In filling your 'go-kit' and making disaster response plans, consider the special needs of those who have pre-existing health conditions. Persons with special needs — bleeding disorders, mental health related problems, cognitive disorders, limited mobility or any other condition requiring special care will need to be considered. If you have family members or friends in medical facilities receiving on-going treatment, inquire with the personnel on how your loved one will be evacuated and cared for in the event of a major incident. Make sure your contact information is updated.

It is important to store extra prescription medication supplies in your 'go-kit' Diabetes, asthma, allergies or any other condition that requires medication can become a serious problem if they run out or are not available after an emergency.

Non-prescription medications

Even if you or your family members do not have specific medical conditions, always have extra non-prescription medications, such as pain relievers or cold medicine, stored in your emergency 'go-kit'. Consult your physician or pharmacist on how they should be stored. Also, keep at least a three-day supply of these medications for yourself and your children at your workplace.

Vaccinations

One of the greatest achievements of public health has been the development of vaccines that prevent most of the diseases that previously disabled and killed millions of American children and adults. Many Americans can still remember the frightening waves of polio that swept through their communities during their childhoods. Although only a few can recall it firsthand, it was less than a hundred years ago (1918-1919) that a devastating influenza pandemic killed as many as 600,000 in this country.

Too often, people neglect these powerful ways of protecting themselves and their families. These diseases have not gone away and the need to be vaccinated is as important as ever. Diseases, such as measles and polio, are still present in many parts of the world and could easily sweep through this country if vaccination rates drop. Each year in the United States, approximately 45,000 adults die from influenza, pneumococcal infections and hepatitis B — all diseases that can be prevented with immunizations. Without vaccinations, epidemics of these preventable diseases could return, resulting in tragic and unnecessary illness, disability and death.

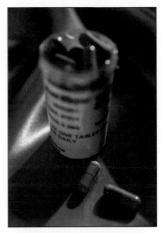

Organize your medications and back-up prescriptions in the event stores are closed or you have to evacuate. 2003/0562484

Diabetes, asthma, allergies or any other condition that requires medication can become a serious problem if they run out or are not available after an emergency. It is important to store extra supplies of these essential items in your 'go-kit'.

Vaccine recommendations are specific to each age group and other medical conditions. Additional vaccinations may also be recommended for people who are traveling to other countries where other diseases are present.

Recommended vaccinations for children and adolescents

- Hepatitis B
- Diphtheria, tetanus and pertussis (whooping cough)
- Haemophilus influenza type B (a cause of childhood meningitis)
- Polio
- Measles, mumps, rubella
- Varicella (chickenpox)
- Pneumococcal conjugate vaccine (a form of pneumonia)

Recommended vaccinations for adults

- Tetanus
- Influenza
- Pneumococcal polysaccharide vaccine

Vehicle supplies

Assemble a smaller emergency 'go-kit' for your vehicle. While your most essential items are water and a full tank of gas, this kit can have many of the same items that you keep in your home except in smaller quantities.

Supplies

- Two to three days of non-perishable, high protein food
- 2.5 gallons of bottled water
- Extra medications: over-the-counter pain reliever, prescriptions and multi-vitamins
- First aid supplies: prescriptions, medication, bandages, antiseptic, thermometer, tweezers, scissors and anti-bacterial soap that does not require water
- Paper towels and tissues

Clothing and protective gear

- Old pair of eyeglasses or extra disposable contacts, if necessary
- Wool blanket and/or sleeping bag
- Rain gear: poncho and/or umbrella

Tools

- Signal aids-flashlight, flares, reflectors, matches/lighter
- Flashlight with extra batteries
- Battery-powered radio

Supply your vehicle with emergency tools, such as spark plugs and flash lights.
2003/0562485

2003/0562488

- Multi-use tool: knife, bottle opener, tweezers
- Spare gasoline can
- Spark plugs
- Tire change tools: spare tire, jack
- Tow strap, cable or chain
- Auto fire extinguisher
- Multi-purpose duct tape
- Watertight container
- Empty gas canister
- Tarp
- Pencil and paper

Vehicle radio channels

Tape the call letters and frequency numbers of your emergency alert radio stations (EAS) on the radio. Make sure everyone knows how to work the radio and put in fresh batteries. Also, tape the channel number of the television emergency broadcast stations on your television.

Organize important documents, make copies and put them in a fire proof container so that you can restore your life more quickly after a disaster.
2003/0562489

Home and vehicle crime prevention during a disaster

Unfortunately, one result from a major disaster can be looting. Take a few precautions to make your family safe should crime increase during an emergency or major disaster.

Unfortunately, one result from a major disaster can be looting. Take a few precautions to make your family safe should crime increase during an emergency or major disaster.

- Consider evaluating your home to eliminate hiding places and blind spots, such as trimming shrubbery and low tree branches.
- Lock windows and doors to your home and cars.
- Use an anti-theft device or alarm to help secure your car.
- Park your car in a driveway or garage if possible.
- Contact local law enforcement agencies and ask if they offer free security surveys to make your home more resistant to burglary and armed robbery/home invasion.
- Keep emergency supplies in a secure location and out of view from visitors to your home.

If possible, have a credit card used only for emergencies.
2003/0562490

Organize your finances and make sure you can have extra cash on hand in case cash machines are temporarily out of service. 2003/0562491

Personal information

Your personal information and belongings are important assets for you and your family. If you lose everything, how will you receive compensation? You'll need accessible records for tax and insurance purposes. If your efforts to recover from a disaster consist of a shoebox, then you may not have sufficient information to help with this process. Organize government-issued identification and documents, financial statements and policies as well as other personal information important to managing your daily life. Keep the originals in a safe place and store copies in a separate location — ideally in a fireproof box in your home with copies in the go-kit and in a safety deposit box. Consider organizing the following items as they apply to you.

Government-issued identification and documentation

- Social security cards
- Birth certificates
- Marriage and death records
- Driver's licenses

Financial information and policies

- Savings and checking account books
- Stocks and bonds
- Recent income tax returns
- Mortgage or rental receipts
- Employment paycheck stubs
- Deeds
- Insurance policies: homeowner, rental, flooding, vehicle, health
- Credit cards

Other personal information

- Health history information
- Will
- Power of attorney

Organizing your finances

During a disaster you may not be able to use a bank automatic teller machine (ATM), go to the bank or use a credit card. Plan how you will acquire money in an emergency.

- Keep traveler's checks on hand for added security.
- Store some cash with emergency supplies. Small bills such as ones, fives and tens are best.

- Leave yourself available credit on your credit cards. Keep an emergency credit card in your disaster kit.
- Maintain an emergency account at a bank with multiple branches.
- Keep an ATM card that accesses a multi-bank network.
- Keep some funds outside the local area because disaster could also affect local financial institutions. A mutual fund money market account in another city or state is one option to consider.

Insurance

Check with your insurance provider and make sure you have adequate insurance coverage for likely hazards in your area. Remember, most homeowners' and renters' insurance do not cover floods, earthquakes, tornados and other major natural disasters. If you are in an area that floods, talk with your insurance agent about purchasing flood insurance as an extra precaution. See guidance on obtaining flood insurance on pages 128-129 in *Chapter 8: Natural Disasters and Accidents*.

Check with your insurance provider and make sure you have adequate insurance coverage for likely hazards in your area.

Making an inventory

Make a visual or written record of your possessions and update it annually in the event you need to make an insurance claim. If you don't have access to camera or videotaping equipment, ask your insurance agent for an inventory record book or use regular paper. As you record your inventory, go from room to room. Thoroughly describe each item you own including the cost and purchase dates.

Make a visual or written record of your possessions and update it annually in the event you have to make an insurance claim.

- Note or photograph high value items: vehicles, entertainment items (television, VCR/DVD, stereo), computer, jewelry and/or camera.
- Note or photograph houschold items per room: kitchen, bathroom, living room, bed room(s), closets or storage rooms and/or garage.
- Obtain professional appraisals of jewelry, collectibles, artwork or other items difficult to evaluate.
- If you own a house, photograph the exterior and include the landscaping. It may not be insurable, but landscaping increases the property value which is important to note for tax purposes.
- Copy receipts and canceled checks for valuable items.
- Consider videotaping your assets for documentation purposes.
- Record model and serial numbers of all valuable items.

Will

Although thinking about your death is uncomfortable, making a will is the only way to make sure your property and possessions are passed on as you wish.

Although thinking about your death is uncomfortable, making a will is the only way to make sure your property and possessions are passed on as you wish. The following are some arrangements you can include (but are not limited to):

- Settle your estate.
- Set up trusts for dependents or donate to charities.
- Name guardians for your dependents.
- Communicate your wish regarding life support.

When you make a will, be sure to include provisions for every aspect of your wishes and that you update your will frequently to include common life changes, such as births, divorces or changes in your financial status.

Information security: physical and electronic

Ensure that your personal information is both physically and electronically secure.

Ensure that your personal information is both physically and electronically secure. Be very cautious when giving out vital information over the Internet (credit card numbers, bank or debit account numbers). In all cases, take care when giving any sensitive information over the Internet.

Protecting your Social Security number

Protect your Social Security number whenever possible. Times when you are required to give your Social Security number include:

- Income tax records
- Medical records
- Credit bureau reports
- College records
- Loan applications
- Vehicle registrations

It is good to ensure that businesses and government sites that provide these online services are both legitimate and secure in collecting your vital information. Questions can be filed directly with the agency or with your local Better Business Bureau.

When you should refuse to give out your Social Security number

- Over the phone
- On your driver's license
- As identification for store purchases or refunds
- As general use information or identification

- On personal checks
- For club memberships

Over the years, identity theft and use of false or stolen identity to open fraudulent and often damaging accounts has become a major problem. Protecting your Social Security number as well as your other vital information — address, date of birth, mother's maiden name — can help reduce your risk for this kind of crime. As mentioned in this chapter, keep original important government, financial and personal documents in a fireproof lock box with copies in your 'go-kit' and if possible, in a safety-deposit box.

Purchase and renew virus protection software to protect your files and computer.
2003/0562492

Computer password protection

Keep your computer password either only to yourself or others you most trust. This can help prevent invasion of privacy or theft of your personal documents and any vital information stored on your computer. It is important to use passwords that are not commonly known or easily obtained, such as: birthdays, children's names, partners names, celebrities, favorite sports teams, favorite places, your name, pet names or simple numerical sequences like 12345.

Use passwords that are not commonly known or easily obtained, such as: birthdays, children's names, partners names, celebrities, favorite sports teams, favorite places, your name, pet names or simple numerical sequences like 12345.

Tips to protect your password(s)

- NEVER share passwords with anyone at work, even your most trusted colleagues.
- CHANGE passwords every month.
- Make sure passwords are at least eight digits in length and include a number.
- Ensure passwords are not set to system defaults.
- Always turn off your computer when you are done.
- Do not share passwords with service providers. If they are legitimate, they won't ask.
- Don't use the same password for everything.

Viruses

The first line of protection against viruses is prevention. Overall, the best way to prevent viruses is limit access to your computer. Consider downloading anti-virus software upgrades as often as possible from an anti-virus software vendor website. Anti-viral software is a good but not a full defense against viruses. Be careful about disks and CD-Roms that you have used on multiple computers. Remain watchful for attached items sent by email without text, under suspicious headings or with files that have '.exe' in its subject description.

Virus Warning Websites

Anti-viral software is a good but not a full defense against viruses. The following sites may be useful in verifying virus warnings:

- CERT
  www.cert.org
- Symantec
  www.symantec.com
- Network associates
  www.nai.com

51

In addition it is a good idea to back up your files on a regular basis. For this purpose, never assume that a file saved in an email is safe.

If you believe a virus has infected your computer, shut it down and contact a local computer vendor for assistance. It is also a good idea to let those on your email list know that they should not open any attachments sent from your email address.

Computer physical security

Keeping your vital information as well as any computers you own safe is an important aspect of information security. If you have a laptop never leave it unattended in a public place. Store unused electronic equipment in a secure place.

Considerations for firearm owners

Owning firearms for self-defense is a personal decision that involves many important considerations. This section is not designed to provide advice for or against citizen ownership of firearms for self-defense. Instead, it encourages those who have made the decision to own and as appropriate, carry firearms for self-defense to address a few safety issues. As with other safety and security equipment, the use of firearms for defensive purposes requires an appropriate knowledge base. Responsible gun owners need to keep up with safety, legal and other related ownership issues.

Home and vehicle storage safety considerations

Firearms and ammunition should be properly secured at all times. There are many devices for your home and vehicle that help you store firearms and ammunition safely and still allow you to reach them quickly in the event of an emergency. Protect your firearms and ammunition from theft and keep them stored securely away from children and adults who might hurt themselves in handling them.

Training

Check with local law enforcement agencies or quality private firearm training centers to see if they offer civilian firearms training. Courses typically cover how to use firearms safely and laws concerning the use of deadly force. For example, you must know how to carry a weapon safely and securely in a holster of quality construction.

Legal considerations

Laws vary from state to state and many states have specific statutes prohibiting the possession of firearms (even with a permit) at schools, government buildings and other locations. In most areas, the district or state attorney's office (or equivalent state agency) can provide information on

As with other safety and security equipment, the use of firearms for defensive purposes requires an appropriate knowledge base.

Make sure you know what is legal or illegal about firearm ownership in your state including the use of force.

ownership, possession and the use of force. If you travel outside your state, make sure you understand the firearms laws in each state you plan to visit. Also, many employers have policies about possessing weapons on their property. Before you take firearms to your workplace, check your organization's employee policy manual to see what it allows or prohibits.

Training and volunteering

Families can benefit from having member who is trained in home safety, first aid and CPR. Having a basic understanding of the proper use of emergency equipment is helpful as well. It is important to know how to operate a fire extinguisher to understand how to shut off electricity, water, or gas supply to your house. Other helpful training can include disaster preparedness and response.

Where can I find training to help with disaster relief?

Make sure that you first take care of yourself and your family before volunteering to assist others during a disaster. If you've ever flown on a commercial flight and listened to the safety briefing, you probably remember hearing the flight crew stress the importance of securing your oxygen mask before helping others during an emergency. That philosophy is very important. If you are healthy and all set at home, then there are many organizations that need and want your talents. Most of the agencies that provide training will also have volunteer opportunities. The listing of agencies identified in *Chapter 2: Government Protection: Who Does What and What to Expect* can provide training on almost any area of disaster management and response.

How can I help without taxing the system?

By joining community volunteer agencies you can provide much needed community assistance while gaining valuable training, skills and experience. The knowledge that you gain from this kind of training will help in being be as helpful as possible after a disaster.

In most disasters, if responders are seeking help, they will send out a notice through the media with specific requests for helpers, clothing or whatever the situation requires. If you cannot find official information on volunteering, call your local emergency management agency and ask for the volunteer coordinator's number or look it up on the agency's web site. If there is not a volunteer coordinator, then simply ask if you could mail in or give your contact information and a brief, written description of your services. Try not to go into a lengthy conversation about your skills because their time is very limited. Remember, any conversation that you have ties up limited time spent helping victims.

Emmitsburg, MD, March 10, 2003 — FEMA's National Emergency Training Center is the site for dozens of classes, including sessions that train Community Emergency Response Team (CERT) leaders from across the country. CERT is an important tool for local emergency managers. Source: photo by Jocelyn Augustino, FEMA News Photo. 2003/0562494

In most disasters, if responders are seeking help, they will send out a notice through the media with specific requests for helpers, clothing or whatever the situation requires.

Quiz yourself, family and friends

1. When preparing for a disaster what are four locations/areas you need to consider and prepare?

2. True or False? All safe rooms are the same for every emergency.

3. You should evacuate when:

    A. You are afraid.

    B. A disaster strikes.

    C. You receive an order to evacuate or there is no safe shelter nearby during an emergency.

    D. You are exposed to hazardous materials.

4. You should shelter-in-place when:

    A. Everyone else is seeking shelter.

    B. You are afraid.

    C. The buildings above and around you are in danger of collapse.

    D. When seeking shelter will provide you with more safety than evacuation would.

5. What are the three types of documentation that you should organize and put in a fireproof area with your 'go-kit?'

Find out the answers to the Chapter 3 quiz on page 200.

We entrust our children to schools for more than half of each working day throughout the majority of the year.
2003/0564681

Part Two **Chapter 4**

School Safety: Have You Done Your Homework?

"It could happen here. . .What we were led to believe would work, did work and it prevented what could have been a horrific tragedy," said Frederick M. Kalisz Jr, Mayor of New Bedford, Massachusetts about foiled student plans to commit school violence."

Safe school planning needs to be important to everyone: school staff, parents, students and local government public safety agencies.

"Shaken but Unharmed, Mass. School Says, 'The System Worked'," by Pamela Ferdinand, *Washington Post*, December 27, 2001

Introduction

We entrust our children to schools for more than half of each working day throughout the majority of the year. As parents, guardians and students, we have put our trust in schools, often assuming that they are prepared for a variety of emergencies. Every parent/guardian should know what to do when the school is involved in a crisis. This starts with making sure your child feels safe while traveling to and from school and attending classes and activities.

Back to school safety

Throughout the school year, make sure your children understand how to communicate with family members, travel safely to and from school and protect themselves at home if they are alone. The Milstein Child Safety Center at the National Crime Prevention Council has developed safety tips to help teach children how to prevent or personal harm while going to and from school.

Chapter Overview

This chapter explains how parents and guardians can contribute to their children's safety at school:

- Basics for back-to-school safety
- Bullying
- Parent/guardian role in safe school planning
- Standards for a safe school plan
- Parent/guardian role during a school emergency
- The media's role in school safety

Make sure your child has a safe route to school or the bus stop.
2003/0562496

If your children walk to school or to the bus stop, plan and test the most direct route. It should avoid parks, vacant lots, fields and other places without many people around.

Be sure your child knows: home phone number and address, important telephone numbers (your work and another trusted adult) and how to call 911 for emergencies. Ensure your child is able to make phone calls either by pay phone (with change, a calling card or by collect) or with a cell phone.

Travel safety

Ideally, children shouldn't travel to and from school alone. You, a friend, neighbor or older sibling should accompany them while traveling to school. Teach them never to talk to strangers or accept rides or gifts. (You can explain 'a stranger' is anyone you or your children don't know well or trust). Make sure the child knows how to obey all traffic signals, signs, traffic officers and safety patrols. Remind them to be extra careful in rainy, foggy, or snowy weather.

If your children walk to school or to the bus stop, plan and test the most direct route. It should avoid parks, vacant lots, fields and other places without many people. If you drive or participate in a car pool, plan to drop off and pick up the children as close to school as possible. Don't leave until they have entered the building or the schoolyard with other students.

If your children drive themselves to school or in other classmates' vehicles, make sure they can easily contact you and road-side assistance in the event of an accident or car trouble.

See *Chapter 6: Street Smarts and Travel Safety* for more guidance on protecting your children from harm while traveling in the neighborhood or abroad.

Safety around buses and transportation

School bus safety is an important issue that many people overlook. In the first week of school, it is crucial that communities know the traffic safety rules. Below are a few simple bus safety tips that you can teach your children:

- Arrive at the bus stop at least five minutes before the bus is scheduled to arrive.
- Always stand 'four giant steps back' from the curb. When lining up, make the line away from the street.
- Never walk behind the bus.
- If your children have to cross the street to access the door, teach them to take at least 'six giant steps' forward on the sidewalk before turning to cross the street. That way, the children and the bus driver can see each other.
- Tell children that if they drop something near the bus, they should tell

the driver before they do anything. It is important to make sure that the bus driver knows where they are at all times.

- Teach children to look around them before they step both on and off the bus so as not to leave behind anything.
- Make children aware of the straps on their book bags as well as any draw strings that might hang from their clothes, which can easily get caught in the door or railing.
- Keep heads, hands, feet and objects inside the bus at all times.

Home alone after school

Allowing a child to come home alone after school can often be the first important step toward independence. Begin the process by setting up simple rules. For example, have children learn to keep all doors and windows locked and to have people identify themselves when coming to the door or calling on the telephone. If possible, have one child check in with you or a neighbor immediately after arriving home. When your children have plans to work on a project or visit with a friend after school, agree on rules for inviting friends over and for going to a friend's house when an adult isn't home.

Protecting your child from bullying

Bullying and the failure of school and police officials to uncover, report and properly address it is one of the most serious challenges to school safety, according to Michael Dorn author of *Weakfish: Bullying through the Eyes of a Child (2003)*. Bullying can greatly impact students' physical and emotional health, ability to learn and view of school. Acts of bullying are widespread in many public and private schools and students typically report it more than school officials realize. A recent US Department of Education and US Secret Service study found a connection between a number of school shootings and bullying. Severe bullying has caused other students to drop out or transfer out of school, plan school shootings or violence as well as commit suicide.

Signs of bullied victims

Subtle and clear comments or signs can indicate the child is experiencing targeted social exclusion. Talking to your child about what happens during their recess, lunch, class or after-school activities can help you understand the circumstances of their school day. This will hopefully reveal whether or not the child is happy, growing and learning rather than feeling excluded and targeted. Keep in mind that many children find it hard to speak to adults about bullying because they feel embarrassed and possibly believe that

Go over bus safety rules with your child especially at the start of a new school year.
2003/0562497

A recent US Department of Education and US Secret Service study found a connection between a number of school shootings and bullying.

Learn about your children's school day to know if they have a supportive group of friends. 2003/056250.

Listen to your child talk about the social 'rules' at school. 2003/0562499

If a parent or school officials are concerned that your child is a bully, discuss with your child what has happened. Find out why he or she chooses those actions, make your child stops this behavior and apologizes to the victim(s).

school officials will not or cannot do anything about their situation. Parents may have to become more involved in their child's educational experience than normally necessary. Both girls and boys can be victims of bullying though their experiences can differ by circumstance and method.

Acute signs of bullying

Physical indicators

- Unexplained injuries or damage to clothing and personal belongings
- Wets their pants because they are afraid to use school restrooms
- Pretends to be sick to stay out of school

Behavioral changes

- Desires to drop out of school
- Changes in school performance
- Avoids routine school route where they could be bullied
- Talks about attempting suicide
- Has taken or attempts to take a weapon to school
- Becomes withdrawn and/or depressed
- Needs additional lunch money

How can I prevent bullying?

Preventing bullying starts with you talking to your children about their right to attend school unharmed and unbothered. They should treat other students and teachers with the same respect. Make sure that your child has a connection with at least one adult role model in the school. Research has shown that students who are connected to at least one caring and responsible adult can more readily cope with adversity. Encourage your children to participate in school activities that allow them to find a support group within the school. Overall, students with a strong support group are less prone to bullying.

How do I address bullying?

Whether your child is the victim or the bully, aggressively seek a solution to end it. It is important to keep open and frank communications with your child and speak to teachers and administrators to find out how they are dealing with bullying. Ideally, this should not draw attention to the victim but rather identify and end the bullying. If a parent or school officials are concerned that your child is a bully, discuss with your child what has happened. Find out why he or she chooses those actions, make sure the child stops this behavior and apologizes to the victim(s).

Talking to school officials about bullying

Speak to teachers and administrators to find out what measures are in place to address social problems related to bullying. Continue to reach out to school administrators as well as mental health personnel and possibly school resource officers to resolve the issue. School resource officers are law enforcement personnel who are trained to work at schools. If you feel the situation is not being properly addressed, express your concerns firmly to school administrators and if necessary, school board members and local law enforcement officials. Consider communicating to the school board in person, over the phone or in a letter to let them know that bullying deserves special emphasis.

Help make schools safer

How can I help make my child's school safe?

To understand the level of safety in your children's school environment, learn about school life as well as the school's safety planning. The school administration has an obligation to explain school safety plans, family reunification plans and other school activities through letters or meetings. Information describing important safety and pick-up procedures should be sent home with you at the annual open house, in the student handbook or through other forms. This information will reveal if school officials have a good plan in place to prepare you and your child should an emergency occur.

As a parent or guardian, you have the right to request that the school develop written emergency policies and procedures. The school should give you a summary of emergency plans (sometimes called a crisis plan) that is typically a long and detailed listing of roles, responsibilities and procedures before, during and after a variety of incidents. The following sections describe in more detail what the emergency plan should include.

You can also request to attend school safety planning meetings where you can figure out how prepared the school is and offer your own ideas on how to improve safety. If the school does not have a plan, or one that has not been updated in years, talk to the administrator about making safety a priority. Similarly, if an incident happens and you feel that the school responded poorly or could improve its response, seek out school officials to express your concerns and ideas.

Keep contact information updated

During a disaster, you should expect your child's school to call you and tell you where to pick up your child. Therefore, a quick and easy way for you to help with school safety is by keeping your emergency contact information updated. Having updated parent contact information is a great challenge for many schools, especially if parents move or if other relatives begin taking care of the child. Also, keep an updated list of emergency contacts who can act on your behalf if you are unavailable.

When used correctly, metal detectors can prevent students from bringing weapons to school. 2003/0562502

Students Make The Difference

"Students have given useful suggestions when included in school safety planning," explains Michael Dorn, co-author of *Jane's School Safety* series. "As a school police chief during the early 1990's, our police force confiscated more than 400 weapons per year from a district of 25,000 students. Frequent student stabbings and the risk of a shooting led to screening all of the students with metal detectors. This was costly and disruptive to student life. Student tips were key to finding most of the weapons but also inefficient. In discussing this at a community school safety meeting, one of the students asked 'Why do you have to check every student each morning?'. He suggested randomly testing different classrooms. The risk of being caught would stop the majority of the students and save time. After further research, we implemented this brilliant student's idea and over 10 years later, student weapons violations have dropped by more than 90 percent. Students, parents and staff strongly support the program that has saved the district more than $50 million. Districts now use this method nation-wide."

Be Involved

"One parent stepped up to the plate at a school safety task force meeting by offering his services as a software specialist," describes Mike Dorn, co-author of *Jane's School Safety* series. "He developed a virtual tour on CD Rom of each school in the district without charge. Virtual tours allow emergency response officials to see what the interior of the school looks like when they cannot easily access the facility during an emergency. This includes schematics, photographs and even video tours of the school. Private consultants often charge several thousand dollars per school to develop these virtual tours. This parent's contributions helped the school system better prepare for emergencies without the financial burden."

In any shape or form, you can contribute to the safety of your child's school. This could range from calling the principal to give your ideas on safety issues, offering to chaperon school activities during the day or evening or providing help based on personal or work experience.

School Emergency Planning

Schools should have plans for the following incidents:

- Environmental: severe weather and natural disasters
- Violence
- Facilities problems
- Public health-related issues
- Transportation accidents
- Terrorism

Safe school planning

What is a good safe school plan?

A good plan should include detailed preparedness, prevention, response and recovery policies and procedures that include instructions on how to deal with students, parents, medical professionals and emergency services. Every school should have a written plan that describes how to provide a reasonably safe environment that will work to minimize the damage from natural disasters and prevent accidents and acts of violence. Overall, the plan needs to be detailed enough to tell everyone what to do but flexible enough to adapt to the situation.

School employee training

Your children's teachers and other school employees should be trained and prepared to handle a range of emergencies. New employees should be trained on the school's emergency operations plan during employee orientation. Orientation along with regularly scheduled refresher training or exercises should help keep all school staff prepared. Many training opportunities exist for school personnel on addressing student-related problems as well as on security awareness.

Emergency response plans

Emergency response plans should be reviewed and updated on an annual basis. Schools need to do this to address changes in staff and resources. Schools should plan for any emergency that could happen on school grounds. In addition, schools should prepare for emergencies off site, such as on school buses or at school-related events either in or near the school community.

Below are some basic events that must be addressed in a school's emergency operations plan:

Environmental

- Severe weather: tornados, hurricanes, floods, winter storms
- Other natural disasters: earthquakes, mudslides, wildfires

Violence

- Crises involving school staff
- Kidnappings
- Civil disturbances on or near school grounds
- Non-fatal fights with and without weapons
- Police chases of suspects onto or near the campus
- Gunshots fired near the school
- Drive-by shootings
- Hostage situations

- Homicides
- Suicides
- Deaths of students or staff members

Facilities

- Fires, accidental or intentional
- Losses of power

Public health-related issues

- Drug overdoses
- Mass contaminations, such as accidental food poisoning or exposure to toxic fumes or chemicals
- Local hazardous materials spills or accidents, such as a radiological emergency at a nuclear power plant

Transportation disaster

- Accidents on the way to a school-sponsored event, such as a school bus accident while transporting students to and from home, athletic events, day-long and extended field trips
- Student vehicle accidents on or near school grounds

Terrorism

- Bomb threats
- Suspicious packages
- Explosions
- Weapons of Mass Destruction: intentional act involving a large explosion, fire or chemical, biological or radiological exposure

Lockdown, shelter-in-place and evacuation plans

In many crisis situations, school officials along with emergency response personnel must make the decision either to lock down, shelter-in-place or evacuate the school. If any of these procedures take place, listen and follow the instructions of school officials and public safety agencies. Their guidance will help keep your children safe and promote the well being of the school community.

Lockdown

Every school should create and practice lockdown procedures. Lockdowns are used to keep dangerous people from gaining access to children and staff in the school. A lockdown could also occur if local authorities are searching the premises for a specific student, group, teacher or item, such as with a drug bust. Find out the school's plan for a lock down particularly in the event

Prioritizing School Safety Preparedness

After the tragic 1998 Columbine High School shootings, New Bedford High School in New Bedford, Massachusetts improved their safe schools plan. The staff received training on the school safety environment and the administrators attended violence prevention workshops. The school hired school resource officers — or law enforcement personnel who work in schools. The police held school emergency exercises after school hours and had copies of floor plans to use during emergencies. Installing inter-coms and two-way radios in the classrooms as well as 100 new video cameras increased communications and awareness.

These steps helped a school resource officer, a teacher and a custodian prevent a violent incident at the school. These employees took seriously student tips about plans to cause violence and school officials notified the police immediately. As a result, in November of 2001, the police arrested five students on charges of ammunition possession of, conspiracy to commit murder and assault and battery.

School safety must be made a community-wide priority, especially if a small town like New Bedford can. Above all, schools should recognize and address warning signs. One student tip mentioned that one of the students planning the violence complained of being bullied.

Schools should have procedures to transport children to an emergency pick-up site away from the school. 2003/0562503

Many times, the safest place for students during an emergency is to stay inside the school or shelter-in-place.

Should the school evacuate, be prepared to pick up your child at an announced location away from the school and to show your identification to school officials.

Resist Your Instincts

In one major school crisis, paramedics had to park their ambulances seven blocks from the school because parents had blocked all the roads with their cars. Instead, go to the designated pick-up site with proper identification and sign our your child.

that children are kept in classrooms or large areas together for long periods of time. Teachers need to have training on how to calm the students and have the resources when their students need physical or psychological help.

Shelter-in-place

Many times, the safest place for students during an emergency is inside the school where they can shelter-in-place. Sheltering-in-place can be done during natural disasters and health hazards. Most students are familiar with tornado and earthquake drills in which they crouch on the floor in a central location, against interior walls and away from windows. Sheltering for a tornado could also include going underground. If a hazardous substance contaminates the area outside the school, school officials can protect students by keeping them inside. For example, if a chemical plant leaks releasing hazardous materials, emergency officials may suggest that schools keep students in the building. They should close the doors and windows, shut down the ventilation and ideally go to a second floor or higher ground because chemicals settle. Parents must understand that if a school must shelter-in-place, they should not go to the school and that the school cannot allow entry during such an event.

Evacuation

If it is not safe for students and staff to remain inside the building, everyone must evacuate. Should the school evacuate, be prepared to pick up your child at an announced location away from the school and to show your identification to school officials. Schools must account for every child present and your cooperation will help ensure a smooth reunion with your child. In many cases schools are prepared to carry out essential emergency functions remotely through emergency evacuation kits. The evacuation plan should explain how students and staff will be transported to a safe and secure site away from the affected school.

What if I can't enter the school to pick up my child?

It may not sound right to you but it isn't safe to go to the school and pick up your child during or soon after most emergencies. If each child's panicked parent rushed in separate vehicles to the school, school officials would have great difficulty keeping order and protecting the children. Responders could have problems leaving or entering the school. Although these parents and relatives are acting out of concern for their children, their actions actually endanger their loved ones. Going to designated pick-up sites is a better option to find your children.

Pick-up sites

In the event of an evacuation, schools should create procedures for parents, guardians and relatives to pick up their children from a location other than the school. Schools should also have back-up sites that can be used if the first site is not available. For security reasons, the location of these sites should only be publicly announced if an evacuation occurs. Parents or guardians can find out where to go during an emergency either from the media or public safety officials, and quickly move to that location. Expect to see public safety officials on scene at the pick up location to maintain order. A good pick-up site should have the following characteristics:

- Ample parking for a large number of vehicles
- Availability on short notice every day of the school year
- Located far away from the facility in crisis

Family reunification plans

The family reunification process is one of the most important and difficult aspects of a major school crisis. The chaos of a crisis and the vulnerability of children can make it difficult for staff to make sure children leave with the right person or have a safe ride home. Ask your school about its family reunification plan which should describe how school staff or designated authorities will sign out students. This will protect them from those who might take advantage of the crisis to approach a student, such as kidnappers or estranged family members.

Special planning considerations

Schools must develop plans to address the needs of all students in their school community. The term 'special needs' refers to those with disabilities and to any unique situation that may require extra planning. For example, if the community includes a high population of non-English speaking residents, how will the school communicate during a crisis with parents who do not speak English? Such special issues should be answered in a special needs section of the school's emergency operations plan. If your child has special needs, ask how the school plans to evacuate these students and make sure that all pertinent information regarding medical conditions, dietary and transportation needs is filed with your child's teacher, the school nurse, guidance counselor and/or other appropriate staff.

If the school does not plan for any special needs, the school risks causing physical and emotional harm to the students. Lack of planning will also make response efforts more difficult, embarrass school officials and open up the school to civil liability.

When you learn that your child's school is evacuating, resist the urge to go to the school. 2003/0562501

An Educated World Is a Safer Place

Joan F. Roche, Director of Training at the Massachusetts Emergency Management Agency describes how public awareness is one of the best services that can be provided to local communities: "I gave a presentation to the staff and parents of a local pre-school who were interested in what to do if a chemical, biological, radiological or nuclear (CBRN) incident occurred nearby. I focused on public education and awareness so, as citizens, they could protect themselves and their families during a disaster.

As parents, their first instinct would naturally be to go to the daycare center to rescue their children if a CBRN incident or any other HazMat accident happened. Instead, I emphasized how sheltering-in-place at the center would make the staff and children significantly safer. We discussed sheltering-in-place measures, such as covering air conditioning vents, locking windows and, in particular, setting up a notification system for parents. Given the parents' instinct would put the children in greater danger, first responders cannot do their jobs effectively without the proper knowledge and support of the public."

Make sure your school has procedures to take of unique needs your child may have.
2003/0562503

High schools must deal with a variety of planning issues and a diverse school community.

Pre-school and daycare programs

Preschool and daycare center programs serve babies and toddlers and must plan accordingly for emergencies. How will your child be moved to a safe location given that most babies and toddlers can't move quickly on their own? Plans for toddlers' safe school procedures including lock down, sheltering-in-place, evacuation and pick-up must be addressed along with other crucial issues involving their physical needs.

Primary schools

Primary schools must also understand their students can also have special needs because of their young age. Primary school officials should coordinate plans throughout the school district and community. Establishing aid agreements with other schools as well as with outside public and private sector agencies is an important aspect of planning. For example, if your child's school will use the transportation resources of a school in a neighboring district during a disaster, these schools must develop and sign a mutual aid agreement.

High schools

High schools must deal with a variety of planning issues and a varied school community. Make sure the school develops plans with input from their community, including public safety officials, emergency management experts, public health and mental health partners and so forth.

Most small private schools do not have the same in-house resources that (larger) public schools have, such as buses and mental health services. Most are unprepared for crises and are unaware that a number of private schools have experienced fires, natural disasters, shootings and hostage situations.

Colleges and universities

Colleges and universities face the challenge of maintaining safety for a large area and a diverse and large group of people. As a young adult, your daughter and/or son should research safety activities available on campus:

Safety issues are critical for students entering college with new found freedom.
2003/0562505

- Learn the campus and always know where emergency phones and campus security offices/officers are located.
- Read about campus police roles and responsibilities.
- Know the risks and consequences of their actions, particularly substance use and abuse as well as dating situations.
- After a disaster, understand that school or classes and other events, may be cancelled or delayed.
- Participate in the safety program at the institution. For example, help campus officials organize a 'Take Back the Night' event on preventing sexual assault or develop handouts.

Media role in school safety

School officials can effectively reach many people in a short amount of time to communicate updated crisis information through the news media. Schools should have a crisis communications plan in place to work with the media during an emergency. School officials need to apply ground rules for interviews with reporters, editors and producers to protect the physical and emotional health of children during and after an emergency.

The National Education Association advises schools to set up the following ground rules:

- **Interviews:** School officials are likely to tell the media that children should not be interviewed because they could be going through psychological trauma and/or feel guilty saying anything they later feel is wrong.
- **Copy-cat coverage:** School officials may also explain that the school will not give step-by-step details of the incident to the media to prevent students from committing copy-cat acts. Less detailed information releases should avoid glorifying those responsible for the emergency.
- **Media pools:** Officials may choose which videographers and photographers for media organizations will have access to the school for image production. Doing so limits the media's access to children and keep the media from getting in the way of any response/recovery missions.
- **Visual rotation:** The school may advise the media to avoid repeatedly airing tragic visuals. This helps students and parents move beyond the incident and begin the healing process.

See *Chapter 11: Psychological Effects of an Emergency* to find out how to help children recover from a traumatic experience.

Overall, schools must be prepared to handle an emergency and work with the entire school community to develop a good emergency operations plan.

School officials need to apply ground rules for interviews with reporters, editors and producers to protect the physical and emotional health of children during and after an emergency.

Children should not be interviewed because they could be going through psychological trauma and/or feel guilty saying anything they later feel is wrong.

Quiz yourself, family and friends

1. What are three main subjects you should discuss with your children about back to school safety basics?

2. What are two ways you can help your child avoid being bullied?

3. Do you have a right to ask for your child's school safety plan and can you attend safety meetings?

4. What should parents, guardians or relatives do if the school is evacuating the staff and students?

5. Is there a difference between school emergency plans?

Find out the answers to the Chapter 4 quiz on page 200.

Your employer is responsible for providing you safe and secure working conditions. 2003/0562519

Part Two **Chapter 5**

Security in the Workplace

"I was too scared to panic . . . I could just see [the tornado] coming through that field. It was the whole sky," said Scott Shaffer, the movie theater assistant manager who led 60 customers to safety within minutes of hearing the Tornado Warning that hit Van Wert, Ohio on November 11, 2002.

You could find yourself responding to an emergency while at work. Support and training from your employer can make all the difference.

"Moviegoers Escape Injury In Sunday Tornado,"

Associated Press, November 11, 2002

Introduction

Employers have a legal obligation to provide a safe and secure working environment for their employees. There are no exceptions to this rule. Creation of safer workplaces has led to a tremendous drop in on-the-job injuries and deaths. This achievement is one the leading factors of increased life expectancy and serves as one of the great successes of public health in the Twentieth Century. Workplaces tend to be relatively safe, however, according to the US Department of Labor Office of Occupational Safety and Health Administration (OSHA), approximately 2 million people are victims of workplace violence per year. Some workplaces are safer than others. For instance, office work is ordinarily safer than being a taxi driver, a police officer or a cashier at an all-night convenient store.

Even if your job doesn't directly involve security, as an employee you have the right and the responsibility to know how your employer is keeping you safe. This responsibility involves making sure that you receive the information and training necessary to protect yourself and your livelihood. Since security is only as good as the people putting it into action, each employee plays a vital role in maintaining an effective workplace preparedness plan. Therefore, as an employee, it is important that you remain aware of the hazards in your workplace and report any safety-related changes to your supervisor.

Chapter Overview

This chapter provides you with basic guidance on what you and your employer can do to ensure security in the workplace:

- Security risks at work
- Self-protection tips
- Bomb threats and suspicious letters, packages and items
- Violence in the workplace
- Employer security responsibilities
- Employee security training

Taxi drivers are proportionally at the highest risk of workplace homicide due to armed robbery. 2003/0562506

Workplace Risk Factors

Your employer should put measures in place to reduce your exposure to the following risk factors:

Working conditions
- With the public
- With cash
- Alone
- At night
- In high-crime areas
- At or near high-profile targets

Top jobs at risk
- Taxi drivers
- Police officers and detectives
- Security guards and police for private facilities
- Executives, administrators and managers particularly in service industries
- Cashiers at late-night retail stores
- Truck drivers
- Healthcare workers

Workplace security risks

Is my job unsafe?

Certain working conditions place you at a higher level of risk for a security incident. It is the responsibility of your employer to make every effort to decrease your exposure to these security and injury risks.

According to OSHA, major risks factors include: working with the public either at a facility or in private homes, with cash (particularly high amounts), alone, at night and/or in high crime areas. When combined, these conditions are conducive for robbery and job related assault — the chief causes of workplace homicide. These incidents can happen at any time of day but are most likely to occur from 8:00 pm to 4:00 am. People between the ages of 35 and 44 are most at risk; youths under the age of 18 are least likely to be targeted.

Jobs with the highest level of risk include: taxi drivers, police officers and detectives, security guards and police for private facilities, senior and/or middle managers (mainly at food and lodging establishments), cashiers at late-night retail stores, truck drivers as well as healthcare professionals (at facilities and in homes.) If you feel that these factors, and other unsafe practices, put you at risk, raise and follow-up on these issues with your supervisor. Employer best practices to provide a secure working environment are explained on page 84.

You may also be a customer of those establishments vulnerable to security risks. When visiting them, remain aware of your surroundings and try to minimize your risk. For example, try to go to all-night convenience stores earlier rather than later, especially if they are in higher crime areas. See *Chapter 7: Staying Alert and Reporting Incidents* for guidance on identifying and reporting potential emergencies.

Terrorism

Terrorists target high-profile locations with the intent to cause casualties, damage, fear and to gain recognition for their cause which can pose a threat to workplaces. Some organizations perform functions that specifically attract terrorism including: government offices, government-affiliated corporations, organizations involving the use, transport or storage of hazardous materials, or organizations that meet violent ideological opposition.

All organizations of this type must consider how well their policies and procedures deter terrorist attacks, not just a select few. Otherwise, neighboring and similar organizations with fewer security measures face a greater threat. Terrorism specialists call this the 'path of least resistance' or 'soft targets.' In addition, organizations might be targeted in order to cause a large number of casualties in a nearby community.

People who worked near buildings that were attacked have also been affected. For example, neighboring buildings have experienced significant damage from explosions and businesses have shut down while the area was considered to be a crime scene. Employers should have evacuation, relocation and other back-up plans for such instances.

Even if you don't work at an organization facing a terrorist threat, you may work near one that can affect your security.
2003/0562509

Is your workplace a potential target?

Thinking through the following questions may help you determine if you face a terrorism threat at work: have terrorist/extremist groups targeted this type of business in the past? What impact would an attack on your business have on the local/national economy? Does the organization conduct business with governments or other corporations that have been targeted? How easy would it be to attack your place of work?

Below is a short list of potential workplace targets:

- Government facilities
- Military bases
- Defense contractors
- Financial centers or large corporate offices
- Healthcare institutions: clinics, hospitals
- Nightclubs particularly in tourist areas
- Transportation facilities or modes: air and sea ports, railways, waterways, cargo and cruise ships
- Food suppliers: producers, distributors, grocery stores, markets
- Utilities: water, energy, electricity, telecommunications plants
- Large retail stores
- Education institutions
- Houses of worship
- Large sporting or entertainment arenas

Working near a Target

Len Cross, a retired FBI agent who conducted the crime scene investigation of the 1995 Oklahoma City bombing, explains the impact of being near a terrorist target: "The importance of contingency planning was underscored following that attack. A major department store headquarters was damaged but no plans had been made to relocate. As a result, all of its operations occurring in seven Southwest states came to a halt and were at a stand still until our crime scene investigation was completed in that building." Len Cross is now Manager of Maritime Security at Han-Padron Associates.

Protecting yourself against workplace threats

For the most part, threats to workplace security depend on the nature of an organization's business and its location. Even relatively safe office jobs can have their risks. For example, workplace violence can happen at any organization at any time of the day. Regardless of where you work or what you do, make personal protection a part of your everyday routine. This section will focus on what you can do to protect yourself on a daily basis.

*Organizations at risk of theft, such as banks, must take steps to protect their workers.
2003/0562508*

Security shortfalls

"During the summer of 1998, I was a bank teller in Lakewood, Ohio," said Melanie Murawski now a licensed social worker. "One morning, a tall man of average build wearing a black stocking mask burst into the bank. He quickly jumped over my six-foot, bullet proof glass window, announced his revolver was loaded and directed the tellers to empty the cash registers. Within two minutes, they gave him $15,000. He fled in an unmarked vehicle parked in the back. The local police and an FBI unit arrived 25 minutes later to take questions.

The workplace security failures were threefold. First, we lacked a security guard who may have stopped or at least delayed the robber. Second, the bullet proof teller window had a two foot gap from the ceiling. This window gave the other tellers and I a false sense of security while providing easy access to anyone of some athletic ability. While no one was harmed, the authorities' responded 25 minutes too late.

The next day employees discussed with counselors any feelings, emotions or memories they experienced. This six-hour session was important for everyone's short- and long-term recovery. Like many organizations, the bank required a direct threat to its personnel and operations to improve security. The quick recovery support, however, was crucial to our well being."

Theft and local crime

On-site working conditions and the level of local crime determine the safety precautions you and your employer need to take. As discussed, certain conditions attract robbery which is the leading cause of workplace homicide. The level of illegal activity surrounding your workplace also affects your personal safety. For example, staff at schools or restaurants/bars in high crime areas are more prone to experience muggings or shootings at or near the workplace. Below are a few ways to protect yourself while working and traveling to and from your job.

Access controls

As an employee, you play a role in enforcing access control procedures. Every visitor should follow the access control procedures your work has in place. Be sure visitors are escorted to places within the organization; do not let them follow you through access-controlled doors or elevators. If a stranger approaches you at the entrance, bring the person into a public reception area to wait. If you see someone who does not belong, report the person to your manager, human resources officer or security officer.

Enclosed or isolated areas

Always consider your safety in enclosed or isolated areas at work, such as in elevators, stairways, basements or back allies. If you are in these areas and someone nearby makes you feel uncomfortable, leave as soon as possible, even if it is sooner than you planned. If you have to return to the area, bring a co-worker.

Leaving work

Regardless of when you finish working, look outside and around to make sure it appears safe before leaving. If you walk or take public transportation, take routes that are well lit and trafficked. If you drive, walk with another to the parking lot or garage especially if it is late or if there isn't a parking attendant. As you approach your vehicle, have your key ready and visually inspect the inside and outside of your car. Close and lock the doors as soon as you are seated. If a stranger approaches you as you are walking or entering the vehicle, continue this routine and roll down the window an inch to speak to the person. Try not to let strangers keep you from entering the car, even in conversation, and never allow a stranger to enter your vehicle.

Working late

If you plan to stay late at work , tell a co-worker and a friend/family member. Let them know what time you plan to leave and call them right before leaving. If you have a cell phone, call home as you are leaving. If your building complex has a security officer, the number should be available. If you feel unsafe, ask your building's security officer to walk you to the safest point on the way to your destination. It is the responsibility of a security officer to protect those within the workplace. If a security officer refuses to help you, explain that you will report them to your employer.

If you take public transportation and work late for a special project or on an ongoing basis, arrange for safe transportation home with your employer. A best practice many employers use is to offer a free taxi cab ride home if you work long hours, especially if you finish when public transportation is unavailable. If your employer refuses to cover your cab fare, pay for your own ride. The extra cost is worth your safety.

If you work in an environment with many hazards and/or hazardous materials, make sure you are properly protected.
2003/0562507

Bomb threats

The number of bomb threats have increased over the years. One police locality in southeastern Virginia reported 235 bomb threats in 1997, 400 in 1998, 511 in 1999, 505 in 2000 and 1106 in 2001. Given these trends, suspicious letters, packages and items, are potential threats to the workplace. Every organization should have detailed bomb threat response procedures and provide all employees with bomb threat response training.

Bomb threats can come from a wide variety of sources including (but not limited to): extremist/terrorist groups, disgruntled former or existing employees or customers, employee spouse or significant other, children/teenagers and others. Although most bomb threats are made by phone, the number of threats received by e-mail and other means (video tape, notes) has increased in recent years.

Searching for bombs

In some jurisdictions, public safety agencies provide training in search techniques and request an employee familiar with a facility join them in conducting a bomb search. Your employer should work with public safety agencies to address whether or not the authorities would ask for the employer's staff to help search for a bomb or other suspicious items BEFORE an incident. Ideally, only professional emergency responders trained in search techniques should conduct searches, however each organization will have to decide whether or not it trains personnel in search techniques based on advice from their local public safety agencies AND appropriate legal advice. Overall, wherever possible, remove clutter to allow clear visual access so those unfamiliar with the facility can search for a bomb without having to go through work items or personal belongings.

Workplace Safety

There are numerous hazardous working environments. Construction, assembly line work and jobs involving exposure to hazardous materials, such as petroleum manufacturing or nuclear power plants, are just a few. A detailed discussion of potential workplace hazards would be beyond the scope of this book because they vary greatly among organizations and employees' duties. To find information on specific codes of conduct, employers and employees can call the Occupational Safety and Health Administration (OSHA) at the main line: 1-800-321-OSHA for assistance or go to the website http://www.osha.gov/.

Spanish-speaking operators can be reached at 1-800-321-OSHA between 8 a.m. and 4:30 p.m. and a Spanish website can be found at http://www.osha.gov/as/opa/spanish/index.html. Many regional offices offer information in other languages, such as Japanese, Korean and Polish.

If you receive a bomb threat on the phone, try to obtain as much information as possible. 2003/0562512

Sources of Bomb Threats

Bomb threats can come from a wide variety of sources including (but not limited to):

- Extremist/terrorist groups
- Disgruntled former or existing employees or customers
- Employee spouse or significant other
- Children/teenagers and others

The Unabomber

In May 1998, Theodore Kaczynski, also known as the Unabomber, was sentenced to four terms of life in prison for a 17-year bombing campaign that killed three people and injured 29. The Unabomber targeted organizations and specific individuals at their workplace and home. The devices were disguised as anything from road hazards to parcels and cans. The 55 year-old, who had the IQ of a genius and a PhD in mathematics, was diagnosed as a paranoid schizophrenic

Source: *Jane's Workplace Security Handbook (2002)*

Bomb threat response

Immediately contact law enforcement officials on receipt of a bomb threat. Provide as much relevant information as possible and follow their instructions. If you believe a bomb is on the premises, evacuate without waiting for an announcement from emergency services. A written decision-making process should already be in place to manage this kind of response.

Call handling

If you receive a bomb threat over the telephone:

- Stay calm and focused.
- Stay on the phone for the entire message.
- While on the phone, try to alert a colleague to call the police.
- Pay attention to: background noises, organizations mentioned, names mentioned, key words/phrase identifiers.

Information to record

1. Exact time of call

2. Caller dialogue

   - The exact wording of the caller (This information can assist law enforcement determine the threat level.)

3. Caller characteristics
   - Gender
   - Age

4. Voice description
   - Mood: calm, nervous, upset or angry
   - Accent: region or foreign country
   - Clarity: clear, muffled, stutter, lisp, slurred
   - Familiarity: known or unknown person
   - Natural or seemingly disguised

5. Questions to ask the caller
   The following questions should be distributed to all employees taking incoming calls and used in case of a phoned bomb threat:

   - When is the bomb going to explode?
   - Where is the bomb?
   - What does the bomb look like? Is it contained in something such as a box or bag?
   - What type of bomb is it; what is it made of?
   - What can cause it to explode — a timer, motion, remote control?
   - Where are you calling from?
   - Where did you place the bomb?
   - Why did you place the bomb?

Suspicious letters, packages and items

In the wake of the Anthrax letter attacks of October 2001, a high level of government and media attention focused on suspicious letters. Suspicious letters, packages and items may contain explosive, chemical, biological or radiological elements. Such devices cause limited physical damage and they are used as weapons of mass *disruption* — not destruction — because they are intended to cause fear and psychological trauma. While the anthrax attacks caused widespread concern in the Washington, DC and New York City metropolitan areas, they affected a limited amount of people with 5 fatalities and 22 injuries. In all cases, your employer should provide mail handlers with special training on how to handle the receipt of a suspicious letter, package or item.

Characteristics of suspicious letters and packages

Potentially dangerous letters and packages can have a number of common characteristics. For example, the delivery of a suspicious letter or package may coincide with the receipt of a bomb threat or other threatening phone call. The appearance of a suspicious letter or package may include stains, discoloration or unusual shape; the package may be covered in dirt or have an excessive number of postage stamps. Suspicious letters may lack a return address or have one that indicates an unfamiliar or unexpected source. Such letters or packages could arrive by courier to evade the mailing system. Letters and packages could also resemble those described in recent media reports.

Suspicious packages in particular can appear out of the ordinary based on normal ways to prepare and seal a package. For example, lumps or protrusions may be visible through excessive or unusual wrapping/sealing. Unusual or overly suspicious instructions may also be included, such as 'open this end first' or only a named person should open the package. In addition, the package may be abandoned at the front of a building or other structure without proper delivery notification.

Dealing with suspicious letters

If you notice the letter without touching it

1. Do not disturb the item. NEVER touch move or open a suspect item.

2. Evacuate the room or area; close the windows and door behind you.

3. Call facilities management to shut down the ventilation system as soon as possible.

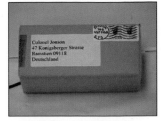

Mail handling staff should receive training on identifying and protecting themselves from suspicious packages.
2003/0562513

Suspicious Letters and Packages

Generally, suspicious letters and packages may contain explosive, chemical or biological elements and can have the following characteristics:

- Has no or strange return address
- Appears to contain a powdery substance or other strange material
- Delivered by unusual means in order to avoid the mailing system
- Delivered at the same time of a threatening call
- Has excessive postage
- Exhibit stains, discoloration or unusual shape
- Covered with dirt

Suspicious packages can have other changes to their appearance based on what is considered a normal way to prepare and seal a package.

Explosion Evacuation

"Following the 1993 World Trade Center bombing, a number of issues that impacted the emergency evacuation were identified," recounts Len Cross, a retired FBI agent who conducted the crime scene investigation and is now Manager of the Maritime Security Department at Han-Padron Associates. "It took over five hours to evacuate the Tower due to smoke in the stairwells, ventilation and just the number of stairwells and the narrow width. Since these issues were subsequently addressed, when the tragic events unfolded on September 11th, over 30,000 people safely evacuated in under one hour."

If you notice a letter is suspicious while handling

1. If you are holding the item, gently put it down on top of a desk. Do not place it in a cupboard or trash can. Leave it where the emergency services can easily access it.

2. Evacuate the room or area; close the windows and door behind you.

3. Persons in the room at the time of exposure should avoid contact with other persons. If possible, they should immediately wash any exposed parts of the body with soap and water and take a shower.

4. Find medical advice immediately.

5. Call facilities management to shut down the ventilation system as soon as possible.

Dealing with suspicious packages

What to do with a known explosive

1. Do not handle any package that might contain an explosive device. If you are handling a package and become concerned that it could contain an explosive device, put down the item immediately.

2. Evacuate the area around the package to a distance of 1,000 feet — equivalent to two or three football fields or city blocks. This may require you to evacuate the building and the surrounding area.

3. Place yourself and others behind obstacles, such as other buildings or walls that are between you and the package.

4. Turn off all cell phones, pagers, radios or other electronic devices within 300 feet of a suspicious package.

5. Notify medical personnel immediately.

What to do with a chemical or biological threat

1. If outside, go UPWIND and UPHILL. If you are downwind, then walk CROSSWIND or diagonally.

2. If inside, EXIT THE ROOM, CLOSE THE DOOR and move into another room.

3. Separate yourself from other persons and avoid further physical contact.

4. Wash any exposed areas with lots of antibacterial soap and water and take a shower.

5. Notify medical personnel immediately.

6. Call facilities management to shut down the ventilation system.

7. Dispose of contaminated clothing in sealed plastic bags.

Suspicious items

Suspicious items tend to be portable devices, such as briefcases, laptops, backpacks or suitcases. Such items could contain: explosives, electronic devices used to set off explosives, illegal drugs or stolen items. Suspicious item characteristics are similar to suspicious letters and packages which have an odd shape and strange protrusions or discoveries accompanied by bomb threats and/or media reports.

Suspicious items are often left unattended in crowded public areas, such as stadiums, schools, airports, shopping malls, military bases or historic monuments. Other identifiers may be that an item's weight seems to be more than you would expect considering its size and balance. Do not handle suspicious items once they are identified as such.

Dealing with a suspicious item

If you see a suspicious item follow the same procedures for a suspicious package on page 70. See *Chapter 9: Hazardous Materials and Weapons of Mass Destruction* for additional background and response guidance.

Violence in the workplace

Employee awareness and timely reporting of suspicious activity are very important to maintaining a safe and secure working environment. The following are a number of warning signs that should help you identify potential dangers. In all cases, employers are responsible to ensure that employee reports are held in the utmost confidence.

Characteristics of a potential offender

Research has revealed a number of characteristics associated with the perpetrators of workplace violence. However, they must be used in context with other factors, such as warning signs (red flags) and should not be used to stereotype people. The most common perpetrators of workplace violence include men between the ages of 25 and 40 years. Repeated signs of the following characteristics can reveal a potentially dangerous co-worker:

View of the workplace

- Anti-management
- Boasts about 'get even' plans
- Job is the core of their identity

As soon as you realize an item is a bomb or dangerous, evacuate immediately and call the police. 2003/0562514

Suspicious items have similar characteristics to suspicious letters and packages which have an odd shape and strange protrusions or discoveries accompanied by bomb threats and/or media reports.

Research has revealed a number of characteristics associated with the perpetrators of workplace violence. However, they must be used in context with other factors, such as warning signs (red flags) and should not be used to stereotype people.

Co-workers who are easily upset and undergo significant job changes can indicate red flags to workplace violence regardless of the organization. 2003/0562515

Poor interpersonal skills

- Loner at work
- Manipulative
- Cannot accept criticism
- Chronic complainer

Personal issues

- Trouble with handling stress
- Experiencing marital/family difficulties
- Fascination with guns/empowerment
- Bullied as a child

Listening to your co-workers' speak about their personal lives can give you a larger understanding of their personalities and life challenges. Sometimes potential offenders may state that they were bullied or treated as an 'outsider' during childhood. Generally, these people have difficulty handling stress. Symptoms may include excessive behavior, such as overeating, substance abuse, over-exercising or preaching religion.

'Red flags'

Knowing the profile of the typical workplace violence offender is as important as knowing how to recognize the 'red flags' that serve as warnings of violence. If recognized early, they can be used to help protect yourself, others and the potential offender. Most workplace violence offenders also experience personal difficulties. With appropriate treatment, they can avoid violence and may be able to stop their hostile behavior.

Alarming actions

- Significant job/site change
- Verbal threats
- Physical or loud outbursts
- Carrying weapons
- Atypical behavior
- Depression and/or substance abuse
- Social withdrawal
- Money withdrawal

Interpersonal problems

- Harboring grudges
- Poor employee-supervisor relationship
- Romantic obsession
- Harassment

What do I do if I notice a potential offender at work?

Even if people with the described characteristics and red flags do not end up harming others at or outside of work, they could hurt themselves. It is therefore important to report observed characteristics or warning signs. Your help can successfully prevent problems and assist individuals in both reducing anger and gaining a sense of self-worth. You also have a right to keep your confidentiality. If your workplace will not respond to your concerns, you may want to consider contacting local law enforcement and the Department of Labor Office of Occupational Safety and Health at 1-800-321-OSHA for assistance. Their website is http://www.osha.gov/.

What do I do if someone is threatening me?

If you feel or hear of a direct and immediate threat, call the police as soon as possible. If the person is speaking in an angry or upset manner, stay calm and listen closely. Always keep eye contact, be courteous and patient. Hear them out but try to keep the situation in your control. As dealing with an armed robber, keep talking with the upset co-worker in a calm manner to avoid increasing feelings of isolation. Try to keep open the option to leave the conversation quickly and contact others in the event the person starts shouting, swearing or showing other threatening signs. If the person starts to show such extreme behavior, signal a co-worker or supervisor for help. (If this person is a customer or medical patient, use pre-arranged duress codes or an alarm system to call for help). Unless there are no other options, do not make calls yourself because this may further upset the person provoking them to act on their anger or threats.

Weapons use

If a person threatens you with a gun, knife or other weapon, take cover and escape to a safe area as soon as you are able. If you are held against your will, stay calm. Keep the conversation going; it is more difficult for a person to attack someone who communicates and makes some form of a connection with the offender. Follow instructions from the person with the weapon that WILL NOT harm you or others. Unless no other options are available, DO NOT TRY TO GRAB THE WEAPON. Look for opportunities to escape to a safe area and report the incident as soon as possible. Do not take risks that could harm to you or others. See *Chapter 7: Staying Alert and Reporting Incidents* for guidance on reporting the incident to the police.

Disgruntled workers at different types of organizations have attacked co-workers with weapons at the workplace.
2003/0562516

Ignored Red Flags

On December 26, 2000, a 42-year old male software tester at a small company in Wakefield, Massachusetts arrived at work armed with an AK-47 assault rifle, shotgun and handgun. He fired the first shots at 11:10 am, specifically targeting members of the human resource department, shooting and killing seven people. He ignored employees from other departments. The 'red flags' included:

- He was seen as having a loud outburst after human resources told him of the garnishing of his wages to pay back taxes.

- He was witnessed as sneezing in a co-worker's face to have them 'get out of his space.'
- He kept weapons in his work locker.
- He showed signs of depression.
- Less than a week before the incident, the subject had two co-workers sign his last will and testament as witnesses.

Source: *Jane's Workplace Security Handbook (2002)*

Domestic violence increasingly occurs at the workplace because the offender knows where to find the victim.
2003/0562517

Domestic violence is increasingly occurring at workplaces. Often, the offender is a former spouse or significant other who attacks the victim at the workplace because the offender knows the time and location of the victim's whereabouts.

Domestic violence at the workplace

Domestic violence is increasingly occurring at workplaces. Often, the offender is a former spouse or significant other who attacks the victim at the workplace because the offender knows the time and location of the victim's whereabouts. It can harm victims physically and/or emotionally. It usually has an adverse affect upon employee performance. If the victim works at an establishment open to the general public, minimal access controls to the facility will leave them more vulnerable regardless of any restraining order. It is in all organizations' interest to protect their staff from violence of any kind. For instance, if customers see a staff member attacked or harassed in the workplace, they may question the organization's dedication to the security of staff and visitors.

Indicators of domestic violence

As with employee-on-employee violence, incidents of domestic violence at work have a distinct set of characteristics. As an employee, you should be aware of these characteristics and aid in the development of policies. These will enable employers to provide their personnel with the protection and assistance they require.

Signs of victimization

The following are possible indicators of a co-worker subjected to domestic violence in or affecting the workplace:

- Visible bruises/marks
- Placing or receiving harassing or argumentative phone calls
- Changes in behavior
- Decline in work performance
- Unnecessarily and consistently reporting to work early and/or staying late
- Unable to remain focused on work or within a given conversation
- Increased and/or unexplained absences
- Third party information

Offender characteristics

Indications that an individual is the perpetrator of domestic violence can include the following characteristics:

- Controlling behavior
- History of abusive relationships
- Diverts blame from self to others
- Extremely jealous
- Overtly authoritative to family members (significant other and/or children)
- Manipulative
- Abusive to animals

What are the options for victims?

The NOW Legal Defense and Education Fund that also chairs the National Task Force to End Sexual and Domestic Violence provides guidance on victims' options. If you are a victim of domestic abuse, seek out your local domestic violence social services as soon as possible. A social services 'safety planner' will help you decide what protection you need and how to go about taking care of yourself and others who could also be in danger, such as your children.

Depending on your working environment and if the offender has threatened you at work by phone and/or in person, you may need to seek help from your employer. This may be as simple as changing your phone extension, alerting the security guard to deny the offender entry or changing your schedule for appointments. The core principals of workplace security policies on page __ should protect you against domestic violence in the workplace. Your employer should want to keep you safe and working as much as possible. Unfortunately, your employer may penalize you for taking off work to protect yourself or going to doctor's appointments, social services, court dates or other places.

An immediate alternative to going to your employer is to seek out local social services and not-for-profit domestic violence victim support organizations. These organizations can provide you with varying levels of protection and support as well as providing you with information on how to best protect yourself and your job.

What should I do if I suspect or see a co-worker victimized?

If you see your co-worker show signs of being a victim of domestic violence, encourage the person to seek help at social services. If you tell your employer before speaking with the possible victim, you may unwittingly contribute to your co-worker losing his or her job. Social services and domestic violence safety planners will help the victim learn and chose appropriate type of assistance. This may include help from their employer and possibly you.

Employer domestic violence protection obligations

It is important to note that your employer's legal obligation to protect and help you stop domestic violence differs from state to state. Several states have passed laws requiring that state government offices create internal domestic violence policies as well as models for private organizations to use on a voluntary basis. Many corporations have already adopted these policies.

Domestic Violence Help

If you have a question about your rights or need a referral, contact NOW Legal Defense and Education Fund, Public Education and Outreach Department at Tel: (212) 925 6635 between 9:30 am to 1:00 pm (EST).or Email: peo@nowldef.org. Visit the website www.nowldef.org.

A social services 'safety planner' will help you decide what safety you require and how to go about taking care of yourself and possibly others, such as your children, who could also be in danger

If you tell your employer before speaking with the possible victim, you may unwittingly contribute to your co-worker to losing his or her job.

Could I lose my job from being a domestic violence victim?

Up to 50 percent of domestic violence victims have reported losing a job directly — or at least in part — due to domestic violence.

Up to 50 percent of domestic violence victims have reported losing a job directly — or at least in part — due to domestic violence. It is important to contact social services to learn about the protections your state provides for time away from work. Although permission for leave is usually unpaid, the time spent to ensure your protection is priceless compared to the wages you otherwise would have earned.

Several states ban employers from firing or retaliating against domestic violence victims in certain circumstances but no state protects against all domestic violence victims.

Several states ban employers from firing or retaliating against domestic violence victims in certain circumstances but no state protects against all domestic violence victims. (The City of New York is the only government entity providing complete victim protection.) If you press criminal charges against the offender, general victim protection laws may allow you to take time off from work to appear in criminal court without risking employer penalties. If you have to quit your job for a related reason, make sure you leave under terms that will allow you to receive unemployment benefits.

Natural disasters

Tornados, floods, hurricanes and other natural hazards affect organizations every day. As with personal disaster preparedness, consider and plan for likely natural disasters that may affect your ability to work and travel to and from home. Store a 'go-kit' with food, supplies and tools in a safe place at work and/or in your vehicle or in a backpack. See *Chapter 3: Personal Disaster Preparedness* for guidance on creating a go-kit and *Chapter 8: Natural Disasters & Accidents* for self-protection guidance.

Employer workplace security responsibilities

The US Occupational Safety and Health Act of 1970 mandates all employers provide their employees with a workplace free from recognized hazards likely to cause death or serious physical harm. In March 1996, OSHA released the first set of federal guidelines to address workplace security.

- Establish a violence prevention program.
- Perform a comprehensive work site analysis.
- Eliminate/minimize identified hazards.
- Provide comprehensive training and education to employees with qualified trainers:
  - Small companies: annually
  - Medium companies: quarterly
  - Large companies: monthly

Security planning

Employees should check with their employer to make sure their organizations have workplace security plans in place. Employers must make their organization a difficult or 'hardened' target for theft or violence. In turn, everyone in the organization needs to be involved and the effort must be ongoing. Employers should ask themselves three questions when they analyze the security of their site:

- How secure is our facility at this time?
- In what ways are we less secure than we should be?
- What can we improve to make it more difficult for someone to break into or even attack our organization?

Typical security inspections assess: the surrounding area, facility perimeter, security lighting, doors, locks, windows and alarm systems as well as structural and environmental designs. In addition, employers need to address general workplace safety as well as other potential emergencies. Your employer should prepare to respond and recover from a variety of emergencies including (but not limited to) the following:

Accidents

- Medical emergencies
- Fire
- Hazardous materials and mechanical emergencies
- Power outage
- Water contamination
- Building collapse

Natural disasters

- Response (evacuation, sheltering-in-place, work cancellation): severe weather, tornados, hurricanes, earthquakes and other likely incidents
- Recovery: overall building safety (power outage, water damage/contamination)

Violence

- Armed robbers, attackers and hostage situations
- Workplace violence: upset current/former workers
- Domestic violence
- Evacuation, lockdown and sheltering-in-place
- Mail handling
- Bomb threats
- Bombs/explosive devices, including postal and package explosive devices
- Chemical, biological, radiological and nuclear and weapons

Employers should protect the facility and, if necessary, use certain technologies to prevent and investigate workplace violence and crime.
2003/0562519

Key Aspects to Physical Security

Employers should have the following areas inspected and secured on a regular basis:

- Surrounding area
- Facility perimeter
- Security lighting
- Doors
- Locks
- Windows and alarm systems
- Structural and environmental designs

Employers should create a team from all major departments to assess and minimize threats to the workplace. 2003/0562520

Employer Action Plan

Employers should establish a secure working environment for all employees, particularly victims of domestic violence.

- Prevention of hostile behavior
- Effective access controls
- Confidential employee reporting
- Counseling for at-risk employees
- Response and recovery plans

Threat assessment team

Employers should create a threat assessment team with members who represent the organization's staff with senior managers from all departments ensuring everyone accepts the plan. A threat assessment team's role is to create a plan to identify, respond and recover from threats to the staff and workplace. Members of the team should share their staffs' expertise to create an understanding of possible threats and impact on the organization and its personnel. Ideally, the threat assessment team should communicate at least once per month and meet quarterly. It should have access to experts who work in the mental health, environmental, law enforcement, environmental, security, emergency management and risk management fields. Often, local public safety agencies can provide this type of assistance.

Employer action plan

Using the research and findings from the threat assessment team, employers should establish a secure working environment for all employees, particularly victims of domestic violence. Employers can take a number of preventive measures that starts with emphasizing a policy of consistent enforcement against threatening or hostile behavior. Effective access control, visitor procedures and evacuation are key. Robust and credible human resources can clear problems before they become security breaches. These include anonymous employee surveys or activities to empower the 'at-risk' employee to feel like a survivor not a victim. If something occurs, the employer has an open line of communication with the employees for intervention and help.

Employee training

To meet the OSHA guidelines, employers should train employees on their policies and reporting and response procedures. For employees whose jobs do not directly involve safety and security, it is not within their daily responsibilities to know every aspect of it. Limiting the flow of sensitive information is a form a security and non-security staff should only learn 'need-to-know' information.

A workplace security policy is only effective if the employers and employees have an understanding of how to prevent violence and support each other, especially people with special needs and their designated assistants. Employee and team member training should consist of — but not be limited to — prevention, incident-specific response and post-traumatic stress.

- Ensuring access control, visitor identification and escort procedures
- Identifying and reporting threats, including early warning signs of employee violence
- Resolving conflicts, reducing anger
- Conducting at-risk terminations safely
- Responding to accidents, natural disasters and violence
- Searching, evacuation, shelter-in-place and lockdown
- Recovering from an incident and returning to work:
    - Traumatic and post-traumatic stress
    - Investigation/prosecution
    - Policy and procedure revisions

Theater manager Scott Shaffer quickly brought moviegoers to safety during a tornado.
Source: Associated Press 2003/0562518

Maintaining preparedness is an ongoing process that involves debriefing after crises, reviewing and updating procedures as well as training. **Training has greater value if it incorporates employee feedback.**

Employers should encourage employees to establish family emergency plans that include procedures on contacting family members if separated or injured, name of an out-of-town family contact person and a place to stay, if necessary. See *Chapter 3: Personal Disaster Preparedness* for guidance on preparing your family to protect themselves and reconnect during and after an emergency.

Employer violation of workplace security standards

You have the right to cite your employer for violations if warnings of workplace violence is ignored. You may contact OHSA, your union safety representative or if it's a direct threat to your security, local law enforcement.

Training Makes Heroes

Emergency response training and equipping your staff with proper tools can save lives. On November 10, 2002, Scott Shaffer's quick and calm thinking saved the lives of more than 60 customers in the movie theater he managed in Van Wert, Ohio. As the patrons — many of whom were children — watched movies unaware of the unstable weather, Shaffer's emergency alert radio announced a tornado was moving quickly towards the theater. Without hesitation, he initiated a disaster plan that he had his staff practice just a few weeks previously. Within minutes of the tornado hitting the theater, he alerted and huddled the moviegoers together in a brick hallway and the nearby restrooms as the high winds and violent weather pounded the structure around them. As three co-workers and a few moviegoers continued to help round people up inside, Shaffer called to people outside to come indoors. Not a single person was injured due to Shaffer's quick response and emergency training.

Source: Distinguished Fire Service Award, 2003 Ohio State Fire Commission's Hall of Fame Awards

Quiz yourself, family and friends

1. What are the six main risk factors that can possibly lead to workplace violence if your employer does NOT train you on preventive policies and procedures?

2. What are the key areas where you can take steps to prevent and protect yourself from a workplace security incident?

3. What information should you take note of if you receive a bomb threat over the phone?

4. If you are a victim of domestic abuse, should you immediately tell your employer?

5. What are the Occupational Safety and Health (OSHA) guidelines for employers to provide workplace security for their employees?

Find out the answers to the Chapter 5 quiz on page 201.

To make the most out of traveling, plan your trip.
2003/0562538

Part Two **Chapter 6**

Street Smarts and Travel Safety

"Picking pockets is one of the oldest crimes in the books," says Detective Cedric Mitchell of the Metro Transit Police Department in Washington, D.C. "It goes on every day, everywhere."

If you are traveling or shopping, be especially aware of pickpockets regardless if you are familiar with the area.

"Pickpockets may have an eye on you," by Edward Iwata, *USA Today*, June 17, 2003

Introduction

Being aware of your surroundings and using simple, preventive steps can help you and others stay safe, whether you are using public transportation, shopping or traveling. For many, taking precautions and being observant is a habit based on a variety of influences: your family and neighborhood, past experiences (or near misses) and/or tips from local public safety agencies and the news media. Crime can happen anywhere and making safety a habit is critical to prevention. Both adults and children should take steps on a regular basis to avoid potentially dangerous situations.

Street Smarts for Adults

Street smarts involves being aware of your surroundings, knowing what to expect as well as avoiding or dealing with others who could cause you harm. Trusting your instincts is an important part of good street smarts. Consider making the following tips daily habit to protect yourself from being a victim of crime. If a pickpocket or mugger attempts to grab your possessions, let go. Nothing is worth more than your health and safety. If you feel uncomfortable, threatened or think someone is following you, leave the area. Ideally, go to a well-lit, public area, such as a shop, restaurant or hotel that often have security guards.

Chapter Overview

This chapter will tell you how to reduce risks as you go about your daily routine:

- Street smarts for adults
- Street smarts for children
- Different types of transportation
- Travel in the United States and abroad

Beware of pickpockets in train stations and secure your valuables. 2003/0562521

Public and tourist areas, such as train stations, airports, subways, sporting events, concerts, bars and shopping malls are a common place for pickpockets to search for victims.

Indicators of street crime and pickpockets

According to the Justice Department, more than 158,000 people nationwide lost $45 million to pickpockets in 2001. Experienced criminals often select victims who do not appear to be paying attention to their surroundings because they are most likely distracted or intoxicated. It is common for victims of robbery and car-jacking to report that they did not notice the perpetrator(s) until it was too late. They tell police officers after an incident, "he came out of nowhere." Prior to the attack, however, the suspect most likely revealed several warning signs.

Public and tourist areas, such as train stations, airports, subways, sporting events, concerts, bars and shopping malls are a common place for pickpockets to search for victims. Since they often work in groups, beware of being surrounded in such places. Understanding these methods and taking a number of simple precautions will increase your awareness and make you a harder target for pickpockets.

Pickpocket targets

- Parents distracted by their children or babies
- People dressed in expensive clothes or jewelry
- Women with loose, dangling purses
- Lost out-of-towners or tourists carrying a lot of cash

Signs of a criminal plan

- Looking around for witnesses and police before approaching their victim
- Grasping weapon in their pocket or reaching for a weapon in their waist band
- Approaching an unaware victim with their eyes fixed on him or her (often from a distance of 20-30 feet)

Common pickpocket techniques

- Jostling
- Spilling something on victim's clothes
- Asking for directions or the time
- Soliciting small items, such as flowers
- Holding up newspapers (especially children pickpockets)
- Acting in any way to distract the victim while they or a partner pickpocket

How can I protect myself from street crime?

Walking

When walking in any neighborhood, act with confidence and move as if you know where you are going — even if you don't. Try to walk next to the curb and avoid doorways and alleys in which a robber could be hiding. Walk along well-lit roads and avoid vacant streets and parks. Face traffic whenever possible because this makes it more difficult for those with ill intent to follow or surprise you.

When you need directions, ask for help from police officers or other authorities, such as a security guard at a nearby establishment. If you are unfamiliar with the safety of the area, ask what areas should be avoided and whether it is safe, for instance, to walk, jog or shop before engaging in these activities.

Confronting strangers

Stay alert when talking with strangers even if they appear friendly and helpful; some of the most convincing con artists are well dressed and sophisticated. Overall, try to maintain a low profile and not draw attention to yourself, particularly at night or in unfamiliar areas. Don't reveal personal or travel information, such as your home address or hotel room number, to strangers. You may consider carrying a whistle or other device to alert others if you are in distress.

Appearance

People can make themselves less of a target for street crime by not wearing or explicitly showing expensive-looking clothes, jewelry or watches. In some high-crime areas, it can be dangerous to wear any visible jewelry.

Securing your valuables, wallet and purse

Carry only what you need and keep it where only you can find it. Try to keep only one item of identification, as much cash as you need and if possible, only one credit card. Many people put themselves in greater risk of identity theft when they carry all their credit cards, their Social Security card and multiple IDs.

Hide the items you must take in wallets in your front pocket or in a shoulder bag under your arm. Keeping a purse or shoulder bag tucked tightly under your arm will make it more difficult to steal. You can also put a wallet in an inner jacket pocket closed with a button sewn-in. Wrapping wallets in rubber bands also makes them harder to remove without notice. If you are seated at a restaurant, put your purse or shoulder bag on the floor with a leg of the chair through one of the straps.

Top Street Smarts

- Be aware of your surroundings.
- Trust your instincts.
- Maintain a low profile.
- Secure valuables.
- Beware of pickpockets.
- Act with confidence.

Stay alert when talking with strangers even if they appear friendly and helpful; some of the most convincing con artists are well dressed and sophisticated.

Carry what you need and keep it where only you can find it.

Filling up the gas tank

Do not carry your cash or credit card in hand when putting gas into your car. If paying by credit card at the pump, put your card in your pocket after swiping the card. If paying with cash, keep your wallet in your pocket until inside at the register.

ATM safety tips

Just as Automated Teller Machines (ATMs) are quick sources of cash, they are also favored locations for muggers and pickpockets. You can protect yourself by taking a few simple precautions:

- Whenever possible, use ATMs during the day. It is also a good idea to use ATMs that are indoors (in banks, malls or stores). If you must use an ATM at night, stick to well-lit, low-crime areas.
- Stay aware of your surroundings. If you notice something suspicious at one ATM, go to another.
- Beware of distractions.
- Keep your personal identification number (PIN) out of sight. A thief may memorize your number, steal your card and empty your account. Never write your PIN number down and place it in your wallet.
- Secure cash in your bag or wallet before leaving the machine. Never walk away from an ATM with cash still in your hand.

Street smarts for children

There are a number of basic safety rules kids can follow that will increase their awareness and lessen their chance of being harmed. The Milstein Child Safety Center at the National Crime Prevention Council has developed practical safety tips to help parents teach their children how to prevent or stop harm to themselves. Children are capable of being independent and confident and they have the right and ability to say 'NO' to someone who tries to harm them. For instance, a stranger or family member could wrongly take them somewhere, touch them or make them feel uncomfortable in any way. Take time to listen carefully to your children's fears and feelings about people or places that scare them or make them feel uneasy. To instill self-confidence in your children's ability to handle situations, tell them to trust their instincts: if their 'gut' tells them so, the situation is probably not right.

As soon as your children can understand, teach them to memorize their full name, address (city and state) and phone number with area code. Teach them to call 9-1-1 or 0 in the event of an emergency. If they become lost, they should go to a nearby police officer, security guard or a store clerk for help.

Be sure to follow safety precautions when using cash machines (ATM). 2003/0562528

If a pickpocket or mugger attempts to grab your possessions, let go. Nothing is worth more than your health and safety.

ATM Safety Tips

- Whenever possible, use ATMs during the day.
- Stay aware of your surroundings.
- Beware of distractions.
- Keep your personal identification number (PIN) out of view.
- Secure your cash.

To instill self-confidence in your children's ability to handle situations, tell them to trust their instincts: if their 'gut' tells them so, the situation is probably not right.

Set a good example with your own actions, such as by locking doors and windows and checking the identity of a home visitor before opening the door. Also, involve your children in planning and practicing family emergency preparedness. See *Chapter 3: Personal Disaster Preparedness.*

Teach your child to stay away from strangers

While only a very small number of pre-teens are abducted, murdered or exploited, it is important that children are made aware of how to respond to strangers. Most parents tell their children, "Don't talk to strangers," but don't know how else to protect them. This warning alone is not enough because children often don't understand that strangers can appear friendly or don't necessarily look scary or dangerous. They also can be lulled into a false sense of security if a stranger 'hangs around,' becoming a familiar part of the scene after a day or two. It's important to recognize that children who are on the lookout for certain behaviors are safer. It is important to practice these recommended 'rules' with them.

When in public spaces, keep a close eye on your children and make sure they know how to explain their home information to security and information desks. 2003/0562522

Prevention

- Always use the 'buddy system.' Go places with a trusted family member or, if old enough, with a friend — never alone.
- Always ask for parental/guardian permission to leave the yard or play area or to go into someone's home. Let parents/caregivers know where you are; return home when you're expected.
- Do not go into a car or anywhere with any person without permission from parents.
- If someone follows you, stay away from him or her. Try to go to a crowded, well-lit place where others can help.
- NEVER enter or go near a 'stranger's vehicle.
- Don't respond to anyone you don't know well, even if the person asks for directions or help; to look for a 'lost puppy;' or tells you that your mother or father is in trouble and that he or she will take you to them

Always have your child use the 'buddy system' and go to places with a trusted family member or if old enough with a friend. 2003/0562534

Response to an approaching stranger

- If someone tries to take you somewhere, quickly move away from him or her and yell: "This man/woman is trying to take me away," or, "This person is not my father/mother."
- NO adult should ask a child to keep a special secret. If someone does, you should tell your parent(s) or another adult you trust.
- If someone you don't know well wants to take your picture, tell him or her "NO" and let your parent(s) know.

Child Safety Resource

For more information and tips on child safety see www.mcgruff.org from The Milstein Child Safety Center at the National Crime Prevention Council.

Know where your child is and with whom at all times.

Let your child know that he or she can tell you anything and that you'll be supportive.

Protecting your child from sexual abuse

Introducing children to sensitive topics relating to sexual encounters can be difficult, but parents should explain to children as soon as they can understand that their body is special and private. Sexual abuse towards children can happen within the family, with familiar and stranger community members at school, in the neighborhood or even in houses of worship.

Preventing abuse

Prevention includes similar guidance in dealing with strangers. Know where your child is and with whom at all times. They must stay away from strangers who hang around playgrounds, public restrooms and schools. No one, not even a teacher or a close relative, has the right to touch him or her in a way that feels uncomfortable. A child should know that it's okay to say NO, move away and tell a trusted adult. One way to explain this specifically would be that no one should touch them in the parts of their body covered by their bathing suit, nor should they touch anyone else in those areas.

You can also take direct actions to prevent sexual abuse. Don't force children to kiss or hug or sit on an adult's lap, especially if they don't want to. This gives them control and teaches them that they have the right to refuse someone from touching them. Let your child know that he or she can tell you anything and that you will be supportive.

Signs of sexual abuse

Be aware of changes in your child's behavior that could signal sexual abuse.

Actions

- Sudden secretiveness
- Withdrawal from activities
- Refusal to go to school
- Unexplained hostility or increased anxiety toward a favorite babysitter or relative

Physical signs

- Bed-wetting
- Loss of appetite
- Venereal disease
- Nightmares
- Complaints of pain or irritation around the genitals

Response to an act of abuse

If your child is a victim of sexual abuse, immediately report it to the police or a child protection agency. Be sure not to blame the child and listen and offer sympathy. If necessary, seek help from school officials, the authorities and/or a professional psychologist. See *Chapter 11: Psychological Effects of Emergencies* for guidance on talking to children who have suffered from a traumatic experience.

Transportation security

Driving, flying, taking a taxi or using public transportation is an everyday activity for most people. Although each type of transportation has its own risks, the more you understand those dangers, the easier you will find it to take sensible safety measures.

Vehicle travel

Vehicle-related crime is consistently one of the most common types of crime in the developed world. Even if your vehicle has the latest alarm system, take extra precautions.

Car-jacking

Criminals have been known to target drivers in a variety of ways:

- Offering help to change tires that they claim are flat (or that they have deflated) and then stealing the car and/or possessions
- Asking for assistance and then stealing the car and/or possessions
- Causing an accident to force you out of your vehicle. This could include: forcing you off the road, bumping your car at a traffic light or placing sharp debris on a road (including an isolated section of a freeway) that will result in tire damage
- Smashing car windows and grabbing valuables
- Begging at stops or intersections

General vehicle safety precautions

You can avoid becoming a victim when traveling by car by doing the following:

- Keep car doors locked and windows closed when driving through busy urban areas and intersections.
- Try not to leave valuables in the car; if you must, lock them in the trunk.

When renting a car, especially in a foreign country, take security precautions and ask for specific security features that are commonly available.
2003/0562523

Vehicle Rental Checklist

- Chose a model that is commonly available and avoids attracting attention.
- Check for full insurance coverage and any limits.
- Request automatic locking.
- Ask the rental agency if they have any recommended safety tips specific to the area, for example, areas to avoid.
- Cover up the Vehicle Identification Number (VIN) if on a sticker on the front dashboard or if clearly visible elsewhere.

Driving in a new area can be very confusing. Be sure to drive to safe and well-lit areas before checking maps.
2003/0562524

- When parking, select a safe, populated and well-lit area. For example, broken glass from car windows scattered on the pavement is not a good sign.
- Before checking maps, be sure to drive to safe and well-lit areas. In high crime areas, stopping your car and reading a map can alert street criminals to the fact that you are not familiar with your surroundings.
- Drive in the center lane of multiple lane roads — this makes it more difficult for an attacker to force your car off the road.

What can I do if I have problems on the road?

If your car breaks down, don't leave your car. Ask those who may stop to help to go to the nearest service station and report your difficulties. Don't park or exit the car if suspicious individuals are nearby.

If you think someone is following you, drive to a police station, hotel or other public place. If you have a cell phone, call the police and give them as much information as possible about the suspicious vehicle: color, make, model, license plate number and description of occupants. This action alone — particularly if those following you notice that you are on the phone — can prevent an incident. If you are traveling alone and another car bumps into you, go directly to the nearest service or police station.

Air travel

Since the September 11, 2001, terrorist attacks on the United States, security checks of both people and luggage are more strict and comprehensive. You can do a few simple things when flying to help security personnel and to keep yourself and your possessions safer.

Going through security

To speed up progress though security checkpoints, place keys, cell phones, personal digital assistants (PDAs), change, watches and other metal items in your carry-on luggage before going through to the metal-detector. Doing so reduces the chance that security personnel will need to check you with a hand wand. Wear shoes without metal inserts/plates in the soles as they will set off the metal detector and require additional security checks. NEVER joke about weapons and/or explosives. If an airport employee hears you or one of your party talking about this, you will be arrested and questioned.

Keep an eye on your bags

While airport security personnel make every effort to clear you through security in an efficient manner, their primary purpose is to make sure that weapons or contraband do not go into the secure area of the terminal. This job alone requires most of their attention many times making other criminal operations go unnoticed. Many criminals that operate in airports use a number of techniques to lift valuable electronic equipment, jewelry cases and other valuables off the conveyer past the x-ray unit.

Put an identification label (not including your name) on the outside of your bags and laptop computer to avoid confusion (and potential theft) while you are going through security checkpoints. Remain at the entrance of the metal detector until your bags have gone through the x-ray machine and never let luggage out of your sight. If traveling with a companion, make plans ahead of time for the person with the least carry-on items to go through security first. This person can provide an additional set of eyes to watch your luggage while the other is clearing security.

In-flight

Always follow security instructions. The flight staff and any security personnel are responsible for keeping you and your family safe. Help them do their job. If possible, request a seat in the middle of the aircraft and next to the window or in the middle of a row instead of the aisle seat. If there is a hijacking, your aim should be to maintain as low a profile as possible and to avoid drawing the attention of the hijackers, who usually position themselves at the front and the back of the aircraft. The hijackers may or may not want to negotiate with the authorities and land safely. In the rare chance that you find yourself in such a situation, remain calm and fight back only as a last resort.

Keep carry-on luggage beneath the seat instead of in the overhead compartment. Doing so will help you better keep track of your possessions.

While the aircraft is in flight, always keep your safety belt fastened even if the 'fasten safety belt' light is off. Passengers not wearing safety belts have experienced injuries when the aircraft hit unexpected turbulence or wind shear.

Cruise trips

Cruise companies must have security planning and response procedures that includes access controls and contingencies in the event of an incident. Considering staff on cruise lines are international, their language skills vary. Make sure you know how to report and evacuate during an incident. When you arrive in your cabin, protect your belongings as described in the hotel safety section on page 102. Be sure to attend the safety briefings and read all safety procedures provided in your room.

When traveling by plane, keep an eye on your bags at all times to avoid theft and causing a security concern regarding abandoned baggage. 2003/0562538

Many criminals who operate in airports use a number of techniques to lift valuable electronic equipment, jewelry cases and other valuables off the conveyer past the x-ray unit.

Be sure to attend safety briefings while on a cruise. 2003/056235

When arriving at the various ports-of-call on a cruise, be especially careful of pickpockets as many port cities — regardless of the country — attract crime.

Personal safety on public transportation

Sit in occupied cars while traveling on a subway or train.
2003/0562526

Most criminal incidents on public transportation (buses, trains, subways) occur at night. Crowded, busy public transportation hubs, such as train, subway and bus stations are a common place for muggers and other street criminals to find their victims. Always keep track of your belongings and never leave luggage unattended. Even if your luggage is not stolen, the authorities may consider it suspicious and have it destroyed.

Whenever possible, avoid traveling alone on public transportation at night, particularly on unfamiliar routes. While traveling by train or subway, only enter and remain in occupied cars. Try to sit near an exit in order to leave quickly in case of an emergency. If there are no seats near a door, sit near the conductor/driver.

Before entering a cab, find out the fee and if known, explain the route to the driver.
2003/0562527

When on a train, particularly abroad, always lock your compartment door. If you're traveling at night and are unable to lock the door, tie your luggage down and sleep on top of it. Do not accept food or drink from strangers. Criminals have been known to drug victims' food and drinks. In some parts of the world, criminals have sprayed sleeping gas under compartment doors and then robbed or attacked the occupants. Overall, be aware of those around you and don't hesitate to alert the authorities to suspicious activity.

It Can Happen to Anyone

A Sergeant from the Los Angeles Police Department hailed a taxi at Reagan National Airport when he and his wife arrived to attend a United States Department of Justice think tank meeting. The cab driver placed the couples' luggage in the cab, jumped in and sped away.

Source: LTC Robert Domenici Program Coordinator, Homeland Security Exercise & Evaluation, New York State WMD Task Force

Taxis

The majority of taxi experiences are routine: the passenger explains the destination and pays a fee based on a meter or a zone system at the end of the trip. Taking precautions before entering the taxi can help to ensure this is exactly what happens. Consider asking the fee amount for your destination before entering the car. If it seems too high, decide if you want to negotiate or select another taxi. If familiar with the area, suggest the route you want the taxi to take before entering the car. Some taxi drivers may refuse to go your suggested route, even if the policy is to follow the customers' request. Take note of the driver's name, taxi certification and vehicle license numbers in the event you need to report an incident.

Use marked and licensed taxis
Unlicensed or unmarked taxis often lack insurance coverage, leaving you without compensation or medical coverage if an accident happens.

Unlicensed taxis will likely not be maintained to the same standard as regulated taxis, nor will the drivers have passed the tests required for those driving licensed cabs. Since they will not have this insurance or certification information readily available, identifying the driver and the vehicle if anything does go wrong will be more difficult for you and the police.

When leaving a hotel by taxi, arrange for the hotel to book the taxi with a reputable firm. Before you enter, check to make certain it is the correct taxi.

How should I respond to a bad experience?

You can take steps to contact authorities or shorten the ride if your taxi driver is acting suspiciously. For example, if a taxi drive were to take you into deserted areas, claim it is a short cut or stop before your destination and demand additional payment, the situation could quickly become worrisome. Mostly outside of the United States, cab drivers have taken passengers to remote areas where they have been robbed and/or sexually assaulted. One option is to ask to be let out at a well-lit intersection with open businesses where you can make calls to the police or for another taxi. If you have a cell phone, call a friend and, in a conversational manner, explain where you are, where you're going and what time you expect to arrive. If the situation looks particularly bad, immediately call the police and give them the driver's name, license number and your current location.

It is also important to learn about the safety of other commercial transportation including buses, trains and boats. Buses, trains and boats are dangerously overloaded on a routine basis in some areas. Buses have been targeted by terrorists, gangs and kidnappers in some countries.

Before leaving public transportation or a vehicle to go home, be sure to have your keys ready to enter your home easily in the event someone follows or approaches you. Keep a small flashlight on your key chain to use to find your keyhole easily.

Travel Safety

What should I know before leaving?

Keep in mind the adage 'proper planning prevents panic and paranoia' as you prepare to go on any trip. Fortunately the boom in international travel has been accompanied by a surge in the amount of information available to travelers, such as guidebooks, tourist information web sites and newspaper articles. Use this information before you leave to help make your trip safer and more enjoyable.

Small flashlights for your key chain are affordable and useful in many situations, especially when unlocking your front door at night. 2003/0562533

If you plan to drive during your trip, research alternate routes in the event of construction delays. Such avoidable delays can cause you to miss a flight or an important meeting. 2003/0526537

Travel tips: PRIME

Taking these simple measures can help you make the most of your trip while staying safe.

- **P**lan your trip.
- **R**esearch your destination.
- **I**nsurance coverage.
- **M**edical information.
- **E**mergency contacts.

101

When looking for hotels, ensure it is in a safe area. When it comes to personal safety, there is a thin line between frugal and foolish. 2003/0562530

It is important to be aware of the political, social, religious and criminal environment of the location(s) you're visiting, especially if you're going abroad. When traveling to an unfamiliar area, find out what places to avoid. In some cities, certain areas may be extremely dangerous, while others are relatively safe. It is important to follow this rule even when traveling within the United States. By keeping an eye on news reports and checking travel information, you can prevent unwelcome surprises upon arrival.

Hotel safety

Staying in hotels in the United States and abroad is usually a straightforward experience: book the room, check-in, receive the key, enjoy the amenities and leave. Taking a few simple precautions can make the difference between an uneventful, enjoyable and safe visit and one that turns into a dangerous or unpleasant experience.

Have someone who knows your destination, such as a friend, relative or travel agent, recommend a hotel in advance. When booking a hotel room, ask: is it safe to walk in the surrounding area during the day and at night? Are there recommended restaurants or shops near the hotel? If the answers to these questions are no, it is likely that the hotel is in a high-crime or unstable area. Research the area and other possible hotel choices in more detail.

Make reservations in advance. Do not arrive at your destination with the expectation that you will find a room easily. Even if one is available, it may be in an undesirable area. When it comes to personal safety, there is a thin line between frugal and foolish. Other considerations to keep in mind include:

- When possible, book a hotel room between the second and seventh floors. This limits easy access to the room from the ground and is low enough to be reached by fire equipment.
- Always keep the door locked when you are in your room. When you are away from your room, secure all your belongings, particularly valuables such as passports, cash and laptop computers. If you don't have a safe in the room, ask reception to put your valuables in the hotel safe. Secure any bags left in your room with security ties or small padlocks.
- Always read the fire instructions and know where the nearest fire exits are located (Make sure everyone in your family or group does the same). Count the number of doors between your room and the nearest exit in case the corridor becomes filled with smoke.
- Check the identity of anyone who knocks on your door, even if they say they are hotel employees. You wouldn't let a stranger into your

own home without checking who they are; therefore, take the same approach when staying in a hotel. Consider using a simple wooden or rubber door wedge as an additional security measure.

Personal and medical insurance

Before leaving on any trip, make sure your personal insurance polices are up-to-date and cover your destination. In particular, check that your medical insurance is valid for your destination and includes evacuation in the event of a serious illness or accident. Carry details of your insurance policies at all times and keep copies in a separate location as well as at home with an emergency contact.

It's a good idea to carry basic medical information, such as blood type, medications used, allergies and your physician's contact details. This information will enable medical workers to eliminate any guesswork and improve treatment if you do become ill. This information is particularly important if you're traveling with children or the elderly.

Insurance that provides protection domestically and abroad for canceled or delayed flights, lost baggage and loss or theft of cash and valuables is also a precaution to consider, particularly if you travel frequently.

Keeping your identification secure

Your most valuable possession when traveling internationally is your government-issued identification, such as a driver's license or passport. It is the best form of identification and proves your citizenship.

Look after your identification at all times:

- Never use it as collateral for a loan or lend it to anyone.
- Keep a copy of your information and an extra set of photographs to speed-up replacement in the event of loss or theft.
- When carrying your ID, hide it securely. Keep your passport and other important identification on your person in a money belt away from potential pickpockets.

It is normal for some countries to require those registering at hotels to fill out a police card (name, passport number, destination, home address). They may also require that you leave your passport at the hotel reception overnight to be checked by the local police. If it is not returned the following day, contact the police and your nearest embassy or consulate.

Traveling and trying new experiences make for an unforgettable vacation but can also lead to accidents. Make sure you have medical insurance and know how to contact emergencies services even in remote areas. 2003/0526536

Keep original and copies of identification and tickets with you at all times. 2003/0562531

Travel Information Sources

The following sites provide extensive and regularly updated travel information worldwide.

US Department of State
www.travel.state.gov

Centers for Disease Control and Prevention www.cdc.gov/travel/

UK Foreign and Commonwealth Offices www.fco.gov.uk/

Canadian Department of Foreign Affairs and International Trade www.dfait-maeci.gc.ca/menu-en.asp

Language, cultural or legal differences, unfamiliar transportation and communications systems can all affect your safety if you are not prepared to deal with them.

Emergency information and communications

Before you leave home, make sure you have key emergency information. Keep track of this information either in an address book or program these numbers into your cell phone. Make sure your cell phone plan covers your destination area.

- Personal emergency contact, such as a family member
- Emergency medical contact
- Medical and travel insurance
- Transport services, such as airline travel agent
- Credit card companies and bank
- Embassy or consulate if you are traveling internationally

Other information you should carry at all times includes passport details, airline ticket numbers, credit card numbers and travelers' check numbers, including issuing bank contact details. Leave a copy of this information at home.

If a crisis does happen, whether a natural disaster, terrorist incident, transportation accident or personal attack, contact your family and friends as soon as possible to let them know what has happened and that you are safe. Try to keep informed about the crisis by watching and listening to local news for updates and information from local authorities. With all available information, decide what is best for your evacuation and/or return home.

Differences with international travel

Language, cultural, or legal differences, unfamiliar transportation and communications systems can all affect your safety if you are not prepared to deal with them.

Most national governments publish travel advice, country information, entry requirements, safety and security precautions and health information. This information is usually available through the Internet and can easily be checked as part of your pre-travel planning. Travel agencies and tourist information offices should also be able to provide up-to-date and accurate information on your destination.

Governments occasionally issue travel advisories to warn citizens not to travel to certain countries. This information is released through the news media and on government web sites.

It is a good idea to register on arrival with your embassy or consulate when traveling through high-risk areas within a foreign country.

Although more extensive research should be conducted for international travel, it is equally important to assess the safety situations for domestic destinations. When traveling abroad, it is often a good idea not to wear clothing that identifies you as an American, as it could attract hostile behavior. Avoiding high-crime areas, staying in safe neighborhoods and using only recognized hotels, restaurants and taxis will increase your safety and reduce your chances of becoming a victim of crime, whatever your destination.

Pay attention to local laws

When traveling internationally, you are subject to the laws of the country in which you are traveling, NOT the laws of the country of which you are a citizen.

Before leaving, learn as much as possible about differing customs and laws. Libraries, travel agents, embassies/consulates and tourist offices are good places to start. Some of the key issues to be aware of include:

Before leaving for a foreign country, be sure to understand the local laws because you are subject to them while visiting.
2003/0562529

- Use only authorized outlets when exchanging money, buying airline tickets and so on.
- If you plan to drive when traveling, check the requirements for a driver's license, road permits and insurance before leaving. If possible, obtain road maps of the areas in which you will be driving.
- Never deliver a package for anyone unless you know them well and are absolutely certain that it does not contain drugs or other illegal items.
- Depending on the country you're visiting, it can be illegal to sell personal items such as cameras, laptops or jewelry. Always check local regulations first.

Take time to understand if taking pictures of people or certain religious or cultural practices could offend local customs and attract hostility. In some countries, photographing sensitive locations, such as military and police installations and personnel, border crossings and other similar areas can lead to the confiscation of your camera and film, fines or even imprisonment.

Quiz yourself, family and friends

1. What should you do if you feel threatened or think you are being followed?

2. What precautions should you take when using an ATM, particularly in unfamiliar areas?

3. What should you tell your child to do if a stranger approaches them on foot or from a vehicle?

4. When traveling internationally, are you subject to the laws of your own country or those of the country you are visiting?

5. What information should you take with you (and leave with a contact at home) when traveling?

Find out the answers to the Chapter 6 quiz on page 201.

Part 3
Reporting and Response

When you least expect it, you may have to call an emergency dispatcher. 2003/0562548

Part Three **Chapter 7**

Staying Alert and Reporting Incidents

"I just knew I had seen him on TV and so I wanted to report it," said Anita Dickerson, one of the people who identified 15 year-old Elizabeth Smart and her kidnappers. "I am just glad we did make the call so she can be reunited with her family," Dickerson felt. Without standing in harm's way, alert citizens can make a difference in solving crimes and even saving lives.

CNN.com, March 13, 2003

Introduction

People often make the mistake of not reporting incidents for fear of invading others' privacy or bothering the authorities. As with the Elizabeth Smart case, being alert and reporting a possible incident can save lives and reunite loved ones.

While waiting at a bus stop, eating at a restaurant or sitting on your front steps, you could see something or someone that seems out of place. For instance, this could be people behaving strangely, approaching or surveying persons or sensitive facilities. Such places could be of historic, economic, human, military or political value. Reporting incidents that you consider suspicious can prevent an emergency or help the community respond to one. If you are familiar with a certain area, you will probably have a better understanding than the authorities of what is out of place. Authorities know this and seek eyewitness help at the scene of emergencies to provide the first reports of incidents as well as tips on criminal investigations. If accurate and consistent, this information will help the responders decide what to do next. The news media also play a role in announcing clues the public should look for and/or a telephone hotline number to report leads to the authorities.

The information you provide could affect many and it is critical that you give clear and accurate information. In the context of what is routine, any one of the factors described in this chapter may or may not require a call to the police or other authorities. Use all of the available information to make your best judgement. Try not to jump to conclusions.

Chapter Overview

This chapter provides tips on how best to notice and report odd activity and emergencies:

- Identifying suspicious vehicles and people
- Noting and reporting potentially dangerous activity to the authorities
- Helping children report incidents
- Helping first responders arriving on the scene of an emergency

Pay attention to cars parked close to critical infrastructure, for instance under or near bridges. 2003/0562539

If you see something out of the ordinary, try to keep a distance of at least 300 feet — one football field or city block — especially before using a cell phone. Do not put yourself in personal danger and call the authorities when in doubt.

Suspicious vehicles

What could be suspicious about a vehicle?

Vehicles, such as cars, trucks and vans (personal and commercial) may appear suspicious for a number of reasons. It is important to take into account vehicle activity, location and occupants when looking for warning signs. Do not walk up to or enter suspicious vehicles. If you see something out of the ordinary, try to keep a distance of at least 300 feet — one football field or city block — especially before using a cell phone. Do not put yourself in personal danger and call the authorities when in doubt.

Vehicle activity

People intending to commit a hostile act can use vehicles as weapon and/or as a way to 'stake out' a possible target. For example, a vehicle riding low on the shocks might be loaded with explosives or people. A vehicle left idling and unoccupied or parked with people inside for a long period of time could also be abnormal. Cigarettes butts or garbage on the ground near the vehicle may indicate that people have been there for an excessive length of time.

Vehicle location

The location of these activities can also indicate a possible hostile act. Pay attention to vehicles repeatedly approaching — at regular or fast speeds — a facility of historic, economic, human, military or political value, such as a government building, military base, major shopping area or school. A vehicle either parked in no parking zones or on a sidewalk or abandoned near those sensitive facilities could also be a cause for concern.

Vehicle occupants

You may also notice people behaving strangely in their vehicle which can range from less to more clear. People in a vehicle who are armed are definitely a cause of concern. Watch out for people dropping or leaving a package or other items and then driving away, particularly at a fast speed. People forcing others into the vehicle or quickly leaving and entering another could also be suspicious. Someone sitting in a vehicle could be on the look out for another or waiting behind in the 'get-away car.' This person could also be using many forms of communications at once, such as having five cell phones on the dash board and/or portable radios, such as walkie-talkies or citizen bands (CB). Keep in mind that people can use radio transmissions to set off bombs.

Surveillance

People sitting in vehicles could also be surveying a building or person. Surveillance methods include taking pictures, filming or using listening devices and microphones near sensitive locations.

Sensitive locations possibly surveyed from a vehicle include:

- Military bases
- Transportation: aircraft flight paths (take-off/landing), ports, bus or rail terminals
- Facility entrances/exits
- Utilities: water, energy, electricity, telecommunications plants
- Commercial and cruise ships
- Critical infrastructure: bridges, tunnels, dams, power grids, plants
- Financial centers or large corporate offices
- Houses of worship
- Schools
- Communications towers and commercial satellite dishes
- Other non-photogenic and potentially vulnerable locations

If you notice someone surveying utilities, such as an electrical line, notify the police. 2003/0562540

Changes to vehicles

A vehicle with changes to the body could also indicate it's stolen and/or is being used for illicit purposes. Indicators of a stolen vehicle include: expired/lacking tags, clean exterior with a dirty tag, dirty exterior with a clean tag or a broken theft recovery system/navigational system antenna.

A vehicle with changes to the body could indicate it is stolen and/or is being used for illicit purposes.

Suspicious changes to a vehicle include holes cut into the body used to discharge a firearm, such as in the Washington sniper case. A vehicle with gang murals, anti-government bumper stickers, slogans or other extremist statements could be out of place, particularly if near a sensitive location, such as a government building. Lastly, a vehicle giving off unusual odors, such as the smell of fresh caulking, paint or fuel, could have dangerous items inside and could cause a hazardous material incident, intentionally or not.

Do not walk up to or enter suspicious vehicles. Call the authorities when in doubt. 2003/0562541

Reporting suspicious vehicles

What is important to note if reporting a suspicious vehicle?

If you notice or hear about a suspicious vehicle or activity, remain calm and pay attention to the details. If possible, write down the activity and the license plate number to avoid forgetting key facts that you will need to explain. Watch the activity from a safe location, preferably at least 300 feet away — approximately one city block or a football field. Do not approach the vehicle or endanger yourself to gather more detailed information. Report the following information to the local police in a clear and calm voice along with your name and contact information.

If you notice or hear about a suspicious vehicle, remain calm and pay attention to the details.

Sometimes suspicious people may cover parts of their identity. Try to focus on their features as much as possible in the event you may have to describe or identify the person. 2003/0562542

Key vehicle information to report

- Location and direction of movement
- Time the activity occurred
- Detailed, yet to-the-point list of suspicious actions
- Description of the vehicle:
  - License plate number
  - Make/model
  - Color
  - Music playing or other sounds
  - Distinctive features: tinted glass, wheels lacking or with custom-made hubcaps, coverings, such as camper tops, or style of cover mural paintings
- Description of the occupants:

- Age	- Facial hair
- Gender	- Eye color
- Race	- Voice (accent)
- Height	- Names mentioned
- Weight	- Clothes
- Hair color	- Distinctive features (piercings, tattoos, scars)

Victim and witness rights

As a victim and/or witness of a crime, you have rights protecting your personal security and access to related information and resources. These rights can vary from state to state but they are similar to the following rights for US federal crimes:

- To be treated with fairness and with respect for your dignity and privacy
- To be reasonably protected from the accused offender
- To be notified of court proceedings
- To be present at all public court proceedings related to the offense, unless the court determines that your testimony would be materially affected if you — as the victim — heard other testimony at the trial
- To confer with the attorney for the government in the case
- To have available restitution or compensation for damage caused to you
- To have information about the conviction, sentencing, imprisonment and release of the offender

Suspicious people

Suspicious behavior

If you notice someone acting strangely, follow similar strategies as with observing and reporting suspicious vehicles. Your personal experience or knowledge of a particular area will help you determine if you need to report a person or activity. Remain alert and always put your own safety first. Make sure you watch from a safe location, ideally one that hides you from them. Do not try to follow or approach a suspicious person unless it is absolutely necessary. If they approach you, for instance, to ask for the time or threaten you directly, try to keep moving calmly either by walking or driving.

Communication of a threat

Sometimes threats accompany suspicious actions. When trying to figure out if something is threatening, you must consider context and any patterns. If someone says, "I'm gonna kill you," or "wait until I get back," it could be a real threat even if the statement seems only to be out of frustration or as a joke. If a person intentionally displays a weapon, ammunition or other explosives while talking or moving in a threatening way, notify the police immediately. Remember, you must be able to explain your observations about the suspicious behavior you are reporting.

Suspicious activities

It is good to know your neighbors at home and at work for many reasons and in this context it is helpful for being aware of your surroundings. Cases have occurred where people were unaware that their neighbor was making explosive devices or weapons in their homes or on their property. Take notice if you see someone stockpiling or purchasing large quantities of firearms, ammunition, explosives, fertilizer or flammable/toxic materials.

Activities or habits, such as organizing meetings to plan potentially violent acts or being seen with known gang members, could be a cause for concern. As the saying goes, 'truth is stranger than fiction;' what could be a bizarre occurrence may led to something larger. For example, the students responsible for the Columbine High School shooting had written poetry and recorded videos that would have been considered alarming if found before the incident. Clothes worn out of the context of the environment, such as a heavy coat in a hot weather, may also be a red flag.

Report to the police if you notice someone stockpiling weapons and/or ammunition. 2003/0562543

If you notice a suspicious person, follow similar strategies as with observing and reporting suspicious vehicles.

Sometimes threats accompany suspicious actions. When trying to figure out if something is threatening, you must consider context and any patterns.

Al-Qaeda Surveillance

An example of terrorist surveillance includes how, "Al-Qaeda frequently takes detailed videos of potential targets. Video footage has been recovered of an Al-Qaeda surveillance operation in Singapore of American and other embassies and of a US military target, each from 100 yards distance. In some of the footage, a second terrorist is seen providing security for the first," explains Roger Davies, a former British military officer with experience in counter-terrorism and bomb disposal in Northern Ireland.

Surveillance

As mentioned in the suspicious vehicle section, you could see people surveying sensitive sites by taking pictures, filming or using listening devices. Surveillance could also include watching entrances to potential targets or trespassing in a secured area, such as 'tailgating' through controlled access doors or climbing/slipping underneath fences or barriers. For example, it is suspicious if a person is walking around a facility or home who appears to be pacing out or measuring the distance from the curb to a facility.

Pay attention to questions a person asks you or someone within earshot about a place. For example, a person asking if a neighbor is out of town could indicate a possible robbery attempt. You may think you are being helpful by giving out information but could actually be aiding the potential criminal. Similarly, a person asking questions about an organization's procedures with staffing, operations or even the security equipment could be another form of surveillance.

Other activities

Trained persons with intent to conduct surveillance and/or do harm may appear to be doing some other activity altogether. For example, they could pretend to be part of a land or road survey crew. Ask yourself the following questions about the presence of a new people in the area to figure out what is considered normal in the neighborhood:

- Do they have a valid reason for being at that location?
- Are they clearly part of a legitimate project?
- Are their vehicles properly identified as from the government, a business or a private individual, such as a local fix-it person?
- Are their actions consistent with similar crews that you have seen?

If the answers to these questions lead you to believe that people do not belong and could be conducting surveillance, report it to the police. Do not attempt to contact or question individuals that you believe are potentially dangerous.

Subtle actions can be considered suspicious given a specific setting. For example, the 9-11 hijackers expressed specific interest in learning how to control an aircraft, but did not want to learn how to land. In other areas, individuals linked to Al-Qaeda were asking questions at rural airports only about starting the engines of what is commonly known as a crop dusting aircraft, nothing more.

Reporting a suspicious person to the police

In all cases of reporting an incident, remain calm while acting quickly. If possible, write down details about the person and activities because it is easy to forget key facts that you will need to explain later.

Key information to report about a person

- A detailed but brief description of the suspicious activity/behavior
- Number of persons involved
- Location of the suspicious activity
- Time you observed the suspicious activity or if the police need to arrive as soon as possible
- Description of the person/persons engaged in the suspicious activity:
  - Age
  - Gender
  - Race
  - Height
  - Weight
  - Hair color
  - Facial hair
  - Eye color
  - Voice (accent)
  - Names mentioned
  - Clothes
  - Distinctive features (piercings, tattoos, scars)
- Include your name and contact information
- If you are calling from a cell phone, give the dispatcher your cell phone number and keep the phone on in case they need to call you back for more information.

See the section *Victim and witness rights* on page 112 to review your victim and/or witness rights to protection and access to information and resources related to the event.

Helping a child identify a suspicious person

Children need to know how to identify suspicious activity, particularly if they are walking in a neighborhood alone. To protect themselves, children must understand that they should never allow strangers into their home or accept any offer from someone they do not trust, such as a car ride, packages, candy, money or any other item. See *Chapter 6: Street Smarts and Travel Security* for more tips to give children to protect themselves from harm.

If a stranger has approached a child or if he or she observed an incident, try to ask the child about the details of an incident. Explain the importance of their help. If more than one child is involved, question them separately to obtain as many viewpoints as possible.

Alan and Anita Dickerson at a press conference explaining her role in identifying and reporting the kidnappers of Elizabeth Smart. Source: Associated Press 2003/0562544

Being Alert

The rescue of 15-year old Elizabeth Smart depended on the alertness and reporting of her family and the community. Her nine-year old sister Mary Catherine, who witnessed her abduction on June 5, 2002, was able to describe the kidnapper's basic appearance. The family's outreach efforts with the authorities, the community and the media helped create national and even global awareness. Outreach to the media included daily press conferences and announcements on the television show *America's Most Wanted*. Four months after the incident, Mary Catherine thought a suspect could be the handyman, known as 'Emmanuel,' who briefly worked for them in Fall 2001. The family's distribution of a sketch of him led to two couples identifying and reporting him, his wife and Elizabeth in Sandy, Utah — just miles from the Smart home in Salt Lake City. Elizabeth Smart's rescue shows how alert children, parents and citizens as well as the media can serve as the key to solve cases, save lives and reunite families.

Questioning child witnesses

- Have children describe the height and weight of a suspect compared with two different-sized adults volunteering as examples.
- Ask them about any identifying marks, such as: tattoos, jewelry, hair color and style, including facial hair and clothing.
- Try to find out where and at what time the subject left this location.
- Ask if the subject was spotted in or around a certain vehicle including the make, model and license plate number.
- Ask them to repeat the story to make sure they explain the event as accurately as possible.
- Praise them for their efforts.

If their answers lead you to believe they have observed an incident or have information helpful to the authorities, have them explain their story to the police and answer questions.

Child victim and witness rights

As a parent or guardian, you have the right to be with your child while the authorities question her or him. You must grant official permission for the authorities to use any testimony in court and can refuse to allow the child testify in court. Police officers can approach children on the street, for example at a park, and conduct a 'field interview' for investigative purposes only. Police officers also can leave their contact information for the child or you to follow-up. For guidance on talking to children after a traumatic event, see *Chapter 11: Psychological Effects of an Emergency*.

Reporting public safety emergencies

No matter how vigilant you or others are, it is not always possible to avoid an emergency. Your call to emergency services or the police can be the first to seek help possibly to save lives, minimize damage or to find those responsible. How you protect yourself from an emergency depends on the type of incident. For guidance on self-protection measures, see *Chapter 8: Natural Disasters and Accidents* and *Chapter 9: Hazardous Materials and Weapons of Mass Destruction*.

General guidelines to reporting emergencies

Report an incident as soon and as accurately as possible. You can provide more information to responders as they arrive on the scene, such as handwritten or official maps or further observations. Remain calm and speak in a clear tone. Try to avoid speaking too fast. Also, you may need to repeat what you are communicating. In all cases, watch and report any emergency from a safe location.

If children have observed an incident, have them tell the police and answer questions.
2003/0562545

Always provide your name and contact information to public safety officials for follow-up questions. If calling from a cell phone, give the dispatcher your cell phone number and keep the phone on in case they need to call you back for more information.

When to talk to other witnesses

Do not talk to any other witnesses about an incident before filing a police report. Talking with other witnesses can change a person's perceptions of what happened. For example, after a car accident, witnesses many times gather on the side of the road and talk about the accident together. When the police investigate, the group often starts talking 'by committee' and may accidentally leave out important information. Police and other responders need to be able to piece a scene together based on individual accounts. Unique accounts are more valuable than the consensus that occurs when witnesses talk with one another. Often, people observe different aspects of the emergency, particularly if they witnessed an incident from other vantage points. After filing the report, counselors may recommend that you share your experience with other witnesses as part of the recovery process.

Talking to first responders at the scene

Explain key information to first responders arriving on the scene using the CHALET chart on the next page. If possible, prepare and give them a map of the incident location. Always provide your contact information for follow-up questions.

If the situation may require helicopters, give the responders possible sites to land.
2003/0562546

When reporting an incident, try to think of locations of resources the responders can use at the site, such as fire hydrants. 2003/0562547

Speak in a clear and calm voice when making a report to a dispatcher or a police officer, 2003/0562548

CHALET is a general method that can help you remember key information for reporting an incident.

Casualties resulting from an incident:
    ▪ Number of casualties visible from your vantage point
    ▪ Kind of injuries suffered
    ▪ Location
    ▪ Odor
    ▪ Sounds

Hazards in the incident area can include (but are not limited to):
    ▪ Falling pieces and/or particles
    ▪ Fires
    ▪ Ruptured gas or water mains
    ▪ Sinkholes
    ▪ Exposed or downed electrical cables
    ▪ Visible plumes, or feather-like form, of unknown substance
      (Most chemical and biological agents are invisible)
    ▪ Any buildings appearing structurally unstable

Access routes available to travel to and evacuate the scene:
    ▪ Number of routes, such as roads, highways, piers, bridges, available to travel to and evacuate the scene
    ▪ General quality of these routes and if any obstructions exists, such as a fallen tree, electrical pole, stopped cars

Location of resources and where responders can place their resources close to the scene:
    ▪ Upwind and uphill in the event of a chemical, biological or radiological incident
    ▪ Available with ample space for marshalling, coordinating and, if known, maintaining cell phone/wireless reception
    ▪ Where helicopters could land to evacuate critical casualties. (Ideally, these sites are clear of debris and have no overhanging cover, such as trees, power lines, lots of sand and/or large rock formations and so on)
    ▪ Good access to available infrastructure such as roads or fire hydrants

Emergency services personnel already at the scene:
    ▪ Services may be needed that are not currently present
    ▪ General disposition of those responding on the scene
      (Are they overwhelmed, do they appear to have the situation under control?)

Type of incident or indicators of an emergency:
    ▪ Natural disaster   ▪ Intentional or accidental act(s):
    ▪ Fire   - Attack by armed persons
    ▪ Unrest/panic   - Explosive
    ▪ Transport accident   - Chemical or biological, radiological or
    ▪ Utility accident   nuclear explosion

Quiz yourself, family and friends

In the context of the situation, how would you describe this person to the authorities as suspicious? 2003/0562549

1. Do not put yourself in harm's way to collect information. If you see something out of the ordinary, at least how far should you go away from the incident?

   A. 100 feet
   B. 200 feet
   C. 300 feet

2. What are the four main things to consider when deciding whether a vehicle could be suspicious?

3. If you saw the person pictured on the right working at a site while knowing the owner postponed construction, would you find this person suspicious? What would you take notice of from this distance?

4. What should you tell children to protect themselves against strangers?

5. When reporting an incident, how should you try to speak to the authorities and what is CHALET?

C _____

H _____

A _____

L _____

E _____

T _____

Find out the answers to the Chapter 7 quiz on page 201.

Natural disasters can occur at a moments notice during any season. You can follow simple steps before, during and after to save lives.
2003/0564503

Part Three **Chapter 8**

Natural Disasters and Accidents

"If [Hurricane] Isabel stays close to our forecast track and if it does make landfall as a major hurricane, it has the potential for large loss of life if we don't take it seriously and prepare," said Max Mayfield, Director of the National Hurricane Center.

The public must heed the calls of authorities to prepare for emergencies, especially when advanced warning is available.

"Isabel Eyes East Coast,"

CNN.com, September 16, 2003

Introduction

By now, you should have a better understanding of how to prepare your home, family and workplace for an emergency. You have the things you need; you've practiced evacuating. What do you do if you find yourself in the midst of a disaster?

Natural disasters

Natural disasters can occur suddenly and may cause devastation across many miles and communities. These types of emergencies can include (but are not limited to) hurricanes, tornados, earthquakes, floods and fires. Rapid, rational action is the best way to survive these kinds of emergencies. Although local emergency response agencies' officials will provide some aid, they may not be able to reach you quickly. Also, the larger the impact of a disaster, the harder it is for emergency responders to reach or help you. Therefore, you and your family need to prepare as much as possible for emergencies that may affect you, particularly if you are in an area prone to certain kinds of natural disasters or severe weather.

Chapter Overview

This chapter will provides instructions on how to stay safe during the following types of emergencies:

- Natural disasters
- Public transportation emergencies
- Utility outages
- Hazardous substances in the home
- Civil disturbance

Hurricanes

Hurricanes are large storms with far reaching effects. Hurricanes form near the equator in warm oceanic waters of around 80 degrees Fahrenheit. These large storms can occur at almost any time from April to November but are most common during late summer and early fall.

Due to advanced technology, such as weather satellites, hurricane hunter aircraft and ocean sensors, news meteorologists can notify the public days before a hurricane hits land. The US National Hurricane Center is able to broadcast rapid, accurate information on hurricane strength and course through its established media contacts at major news outlets. Even before hurricane conditions reach the coast, tropical storm weather may move well in advance of the storm. Heavy rain, winds in excess of 40 miles per hour and rough surf may begin hours or days before a storm makes landfall. In any case, you should listen to weather radio, local television station or local radio station to receive updated information and instructions.

If a hurricane is moving toward land and has the potential to cause hurricane conditions on the coast within 48 hours, a Hurricane Watch is issued. Hurricane conditions include: rain, winds in excess of 75 mph and tides 25 feet above normal (storm surge). If hurricane conditions are expected within 24 hours, authorities will issue a Hurricane Warning.

Hurricane preparations

Your family or household should make preparations for possible high winds, flooding and heavy rain as soon as you hear of a Hurricane Watch. Do not wait until a 24-hour Hurricane Warning is issued to begin making your preparations.

Protecting your home

- Pick up loose items in the yard, such as grills, garbage cans, toys, tools, flower pots. The wind can pick them up and turn them into dangerous missiles.
- Start gathering materials to cover the windows if needed, such as precut plywood or tape.
- When taping windows, crisscross it over the glass in large X shapes. This helps decrease the amount of flying glass.
- If you live in a mobile or pre-fabricated home unconnected from the foundation, secure tie-downs.

Stacy, NC, September 20, 2003 — Gerald Salter of Stacy, NC calls for FEMA disaster relief amid the flooded remnants of his family's living room in the aftermath of Hurricane Isabel. Source: photo by Cynthia Hunter, FEMA News Photo 2003/0564501

Birth of a Hurricane

A hurricane often starts out as a disorganized mass of squally weather called a tropical depression with winds of up to 39 miles per hour (mph.) If the weather conditions are right, a tropical depression can intensify becoming a tropical storm with sustained winds of 40 to 74 mph. If a tropical storm's sustained wind speed exceeds 74 mph, it becomes a hurricane. Waves can also reach high above 20 feet and winds can range from 75 mph to stronger than 150 mph.

Key Warnings

A **Hurricane Watch** means that hurricane conditions are possible within those 48 hours including: rain, winds in excess of 75 mph and tides 25 feet above normal (storm surge.)

A **Hurricane Warning** is issued when hurricane conditions are expected within 24 hours.

Supplies

- Take out and make sure your emergency go-kit is stocked.
- If you are close to the storm, store extra water in the bathtub, jugs and pails because public water supply may break or be contaminated during a storm.
- Fill your car with fuel in case you need to evacuate.
- Learn about shelter locations and, if necessary, find shelters that accept pets.

Hurricane warning

If a Hurricane Warning is in effect, hurricane conditions are expected within 24 hours. Follow the advice of authorities; do not wait until severe conditions threaten.

During a hurricane

If advised to shelter-in-place

- Remain indoors and stay away from the windows. Do not try leave during the height of the storm.
- Do not leave even if the weather looks calm, you could be in the 'eye' of the storm. Wait inside until officials announce it is safe to go outside.

If advised to evacuate

- Evacuate as soon as officials instruct the public.
- Use authorities' evacuation routes. Most hurricane evacuation routes are marked with blue signs with a hurricane symbol or label.
- Do not drive in flooded areas.
- Take your emergency 'go-kit' and important documents.
- Advise your out-of-town family contact you are leaving if time permits.
- If you live near the shore, plan to go inland where it's safe.
- Remember that when a hurricane hits, a storm surge may occur which is when the sea rises as high as 25 feet above normal high tide. Most people who die in hurricanes drown in the storm surge.

After a hurricane

In some instances, the authorities may advise you to turn off your utilities. Leave written instructions on how to turn off the electricity, gas and water in an easy-to-see location in your home. **Remember, you will need a professional to turn on the utilities**.

Hatteras Village, NC, September 29, 2003 — An evacuation sign marks the route along Highway 264, west of Englehard, NC. Source: photo by Cynthia Hunter, FEMA News Photo 2003/0562550

When a hurricane hits, a storm surge may occur which is when the sea rises as high as 25 feet above normal high tide. Most people who die in hurricanes drown in the storm surge.

Earthquake

Breaking and shifting of rock beneath the Earth's surface causes earthquakes to erupt without any warning during any time of the year — day or night. In addition to California; earthquakes occur in many other states and countries. Earthquake damage, however, is predictable and preventable. Injury and death are usually caused by collapsing walls, flying glass or falling objects.

To prepare for an earthquake, pick a room or area in your house either under a sturdy table or desk or against an interior wall well away from windows, bookcases or tall furniture that could fall. If you have no other options, take shelter beneath a well-supported door frame.

Protecting your home

Taking precautions in your home can save your life and prevent expensive damage. Such earthquake precautions could include simply moving heavier items to lower, safer places or making more structural changes, such as bolting down major appliances and even your house. These practices can save you potential earthquake damage repair. The Federal Emergency Management Agency (FEMA), suggests the following tips to consider.

Objects and furniture

- Anchor high objects.
- Secure items that might fall like televisions, computers and books.
- Move large or heavy objects to lower shelves.
- Don't keep top heavy objects near your bed or other places of rest.
- Store securely pesticides, weed killer, chemicals and flammable products in closed cabinets with latches on bottom shelves.
- Bolt tall furniture, such as bookcases and appliances, to the wall.
- Install latches on the cabinets.
- Brace overhead light fixtures.
- Strap the water heater to wall studs.
- Bolt down any gas appliances.

Structural support

- Install flexible pipe fittings to avoid gas or water leaks.
- Check to see if your house is bolted to its foundation. If not, think about having it bolted. You will not be able to live in your home if it slides off the foundation during an earthquake.
- Consider having a structural design engineer evaluate your house or apartment unit.
- Follow local building standards and use safe land codes that regulate land along fault lines.

Earthquake response procedures

Responding to an earthquake involves moving to a safe place to protect yourself from falling objects if inside and buildings, other structures and trees if outside.

If an earthquake occurs and you are indoors

- Go to a safe room of the house.
- Move under a table or desk away from windows and hold onto one leg of the table or desk.
- Protect your eyes by keeping your head down.
- Stay in place until the shaking stops.
- If you must leave a building after the shaking stops, use the stairs — not the elevator.

If an earthquake occurs and you are outdoors

- Stay outside.
- Move away from buildings, trees, streetlights and power lines. Crouch down and cover your head.
- If you are in a vehicle, pull over to a clear location. Stop and stay there with your seat belt fastened until the shaking has stopped.
- Be on the lookout for fires.
- If you are in a coastal area, move to higher ground because earthquakes can cause tsunamis which are large waves or undersea landslides.

After an earthquake

When the shaking stops, take steps to ensure you and those near you are safe and inspect the damage in and near your home. First responders will be busy attending to injuries and structural damage, thus use a telephone only to report life-threatening emergencies. While looking after your personal safety and your home, be prepared to expect aftershocks.

Personal safety

- Check yourself for injuries.
- Put on long pants, a long sleeved shirt, sturdy shoes and work gloves to protect yourself from injury.
- After taking care of yourself look for other people who may be injured or trapped beneath fallen debris.
- Check on neighbors who may need special assistance — people with children, the elderly or disabled.
- Listen to a portable battery powered radio (or television) for updated emergency information and instructions.

Northridge Earthquake, CA, January 17, 1994 — Many roads, including bridges and elevated highways were damaged by a 6.7 magnitude earthquake. Approximately 114,000 residential and commercial structures were damaged and 72 deaths were attributed to the earthquake. Damage costs were estimated at $25 billion. Source: FEMA News Photo. 2003/0564502

Home inspection

- Check your home for damage and evacuate everyone if your home is unsafe.
- Use battery powered lanterns or flashlights to inspect your home. Do not use candles in the event of a gas leak.
- Avoid smoking inside buildings.
- Check if your toilets are flushing properly.
- If a water pipe burst, turn of the water at the main valve.
- Open closet and cabinet doors cautiously.
- Take pictures of house damage both inside and outside for insurance claims.

Hazardous materials

- Search for and extinguish small fires.
- If you smell gas or hear a hissing sound, turn off the main gas valve located outside and open the windows. If you do not smell gas, leave the gas on at the main valve. Only have professionals turn the gas back on.
- If you suspect electrical damage, turn the electricity off at the main fuse box or circuit breaker. Only have professionals turn the electricity back on.
- Clean up spilled chemicals, medicines, gasoline or other flammable liquids immediately and carefully. (See page 135 for guidance on cleaning up and disposing of chemicals.)
- If you have chimneys, inspect the entire length carefully for damage. Cracks in your chimney could cause fire later on or result in injury when chunks fall.

When outside

- Watch out for fallen power lines or broken gas lines and stay out of damaged areas.
- Stay away from damaged buildings.
- When entering buildings use extreme caution.
- Check walls, floors, staircase and windows to ensure that the building is not in danger of collapse.
- Check for gas leaks.

Tornado

If conditions are right, a tornado can happen regardless of the location or time of year. They typically occur, however, during spring and summer and have been reported in mountains and valleys, over deserts and swamps, from the Gulf Coast, Canada, Hawaii and even Alaska.

Generally, tornados develop from severe thunderstorms but can also form when a hurricane is making landfall. During a severe thunderstorm or hurricane, remain alert and listen to weather officials to receive timely information on the development of a possible tornado. Officials may report a **Tornado Watch** or **Tornado Warning**. Quick thinking and planning can minimize tornado devastation.

Tornado Watch

Officials will issue a Tornado Watch if a tornado is likely. Upon hearing of a Tornado Watch, take notice of the current weather conditions. Rotating clouds, a wall or funnel cloud, hail, dark-greenish skies and roaring sounds like a train running over tracks can indicate an approaching tornado. Your alertness is crucial because officials may only have short advance notice of an approaching tornado. Make sure that you are listening to your weather radio, local television or radio station, community warning system to receive updated information and instructions. Always follow the instructions of officials.

To prepare, crack your window in the event a sudden drop in air pressure associated with tornados occurs. Take your emergency 'go-kit' and move it into your basement or other shelter areas in the event officials announce a Tornado Warning and you need to shelter-in-place.

Tornado Warning

A Tornado Warning means that a tornado has been spotted or is approaching your area. In either case, you must act quickly.

- Take cover immediately.
- Stay away from windows.
- Go to a tornado safe room in your home. Preferably, go to an underground location, such as a basement or storm cellar. If this is not possible, go to a central room, such as a bathroom or interior hallway on the lowest floor.
- Move under something sturdy or use your arms and hands to brace yourself and to protect your head from falling objects and flying debris.
- If you are in a mobile home or outside in a car, go immediately to a nearby sturdy building, ideally to the basement. A highway overpass

Once a tornado is sighted, a Tornado Warning is issued and residents must take cover underground immediately. 2003/0564503

Key Warnings

Your alertness to tornado warnings is crucial because officials may only have short advance notice to warn you of an approaching tornado.

A **Tornado Watch** is when weather conditions indicate a tornado is likely.

A **Tornado Warning** occurs when a tornado is sighted or approaching your area.

Belhaven, NC, September 20, 2003 — House on left, 275 Riverview St., was elevated using Federal mitigation funds after Hurricane Floyd. The house on the right, 690 E. Main St., was not and had water damage after Hurricane Isabel. Source: photo by Dennis Wheeler, FEMA News Photo 2003/0564522

Your state or community can receive FEMA funds from its annual budget of $20 million to reduce or eliminate the long-term risk of flood damage to buildings, manufactured homes and other structures insurable under the National Flood Insurance Program (NFIP).

may provide some shelter for your car. Do not try to drive away from a tornado.

- If you are stuck outside, lie flat in a low spot, such as a ditch, underneath a highway overpass or in a ravine. Make sure you are away from water in the event lightening strikes.

After a tornado

Use extreme caution before you return to your home or enter a damaged building. Follow the advice of officials and consider the guidance for return home and/or recovering from earthquakes on page 125.

Floods

A variety of water sources can cause floods especially around or near low-lying areas: heavy rains, melting snow, clogged or poor house gutters, cracked foundation, inadequate road drainage systems, failed protective devices, such as levees and dams, as well as tropical storms and hurricanes. A sudden torrential downpour can cause flash floods within just a few minutes. Property damage from flooding now totals over $1 billion each year in the United States. Even if you don't live in a flood plain, you may experience flooding. Consider that 25 percent of all flood insurance claims occur in the low-to-moderate risk areas.

Before a flood

You can take measures to prevent or reduce the damage of flooding. FEMA provides funds to help homeowners at risk of flooding with such improvement as house elevation.

- Install backflow valves or plugs in drains, toilets and other sewer connections to prevent flood water from entering the home.
- Build and install flood shields for doors and other openings to reinforce buildings structures.
- Provide openings in foundation walls that allow flood water in and out to avoid collapse.
- Elevate or relocate furnaces, hot water heaters and electrical panels.
- Store important documents and irreplaceable personal objects, such as photographs, where they will avoid damage.
- Elevate existing residences to a new foundation above flood high water levels.
- Buy and install sump pumps with back-up power.

Your state or community can receive FEMA funds from its annual budget of $20 million to reduce or eliminate the long-term risk of flood damage to buildings, manufactured homes and other structures insurable under the National Flood Insurance Program (NFIP).

Flood Insurance

Nearly 20,000 communities across the United States and its territories participate in the NFIP whereby homeowners, renters, and business owners can receive federally-backed flood insurance if they take steps to prevent future flood damage. Buildings built using NFIP building standards suffer approximately 80 percent less damage annually than those without such standards. In addition to helping with flood damage prevention/mitigation, NFIP identifies and maps the nation's flood plains. Mapping flood hazards creates broad-based awareness of the flood hazards and provides the basis for construction planning and insurance premiums. If you plan on buying, building or repairing a building in a designated Special Flood Hazard Areas (SFHA's), you will be required to purchase flood insurance in order to obtain financing.

Home or renter's insurance usually does not cover flooding and requires you to pay for separate coverage either with your existing or another insurance provider. If your agent does not underwrite flood insurance or you don't have an agent, you can call the NFIP toll free number 1-888-FLOOD29 or TDD# 1-800-427-5593 to obtain the name of an agent in your area who does underwrite flood insurance.

Flood Watch

A Flood Watch or Flash Flood Watch both indicate that flooding is possible in your area. You should begin preparing your family and home as soon as authorities issue a Flash Flood Watch.

- Retrieve your prepared emergency 'go-kit.'
- Fill bathtubs, sinks, and plastic bottles with clean water. Remember that a flood may contaminate water.
- Listen for updated weather news to receive information and instructions on picking up sand bags and other items to prevent damage to your home.
- Move your furniture and valuables to higher floors of your home.
- If you are outdoors, go to high ground.

Flood Warning

A Flood Warning or Flash Flood Warning both mean that flooding is occurring or is expected to occur in your area.

- If officials give evacuation orders, leave immediately.
- Follow recommended evacuation routes that should help you move to higher ground. Do not take shortcuts. Main roadways are generally higher in elevation than secondary roads.
- Stay abreast of road conditions through news updates.
- Do not try to drive or wade through areas of the road covered by running water.

Leave as soon as possible if officials direct citizens to evacuate before a flood warning. 2003/0564508

Key Warnings

A **Flood Watch** and a **Flash Flood Watch** both mean that flooding is possible in your area.

A **Flood Warning** and a **Flash Flood Warning** means that flooding is occurring or is expected to occur in your area.

Floods can overwhelm a community and destroy your home and treasured possessions. Prepare your home and finances for a flood especially if you live in a flood zone. 2003/0564505

Key Warnings

Winter Weather Advisory means winter weather conditions are expected to cause significant inconveniences and may be hazardous, especially on the roads.

Winter Storm Watch indicates a storm is possible.

Winter Storm Warning means a storm is happening in some areas or will soon occur.

Blizzard Warning means oncoming snow and strong winds combined will produce blinding snow, near zero visibility, deep drifts, and life-threatening wind chill.

Frost/Freeze Warning means freezing temperatures are expected.

- If your car stalls from rising water, leave it. As little as one foot of water can move cars off the road.
- Stay away from downed power lines.

After a flood

- Throw away water and food that has come into contact with floodwater.
- Check for utility outages and contact a professional to turn utilities back on. Make sure areas around electrical outlets and utilities are completely dry before touching them.
- Consider applying for hazard mitigation funds to prevent future flooding.
- When rebuilding after a flood, elevate or relocate your electric box or panel above flood damage.
- Elevate or relocate your furnace, water heater and major appliances to a base of masonry or pressure treated lumber. They can be relocated out of the flood danger by moving them to the first floor.
- Elevate or relocate your heat pump or air conditioner.
- Stop sewer backup by installing a floor drain plug. Commercial plugs are available that can be placed in the floor drain below the grate. A plug not only stops water from entering the house but it prevents it from leaving the house as well.
- Install an interior flood wall of concrete blocks or poured concrete to protect heating systems.

Severe winter weather

Since many communities deal with severe winter weather on a regular basis, people often do not take as many precautions in their home or car and/or take the weather warnings as seriously as they should. The first step is to understand the various weather warnings. A Winter Weather Advisory means winter weather conditions are expected to cause significant inconveniences and may be hazardous, especially on the roads. Next, a Winter Storm Watch indicates a storm is possible. Be alert while driving and make preparations, such as stocking extra food and water. A Winter Storm Warning means a storm is happening in some areas or will soon occur and you should stay in doors as much as possible. A Blizzard Warning indicates a combination of oncoming snow and strong winds will produce blinding snow, near zero visibility, deep drifts and life-threatening wind chill. You should go in doors as soon as possible. Lastly, a Frost/Freeze Warning means freezing temperatures are expected. FEMA provides comprehensive winter storm tips for before, during and after severe weather.

Before a winter storm

Know ahead of time what you will do to help elderly or disabled friends and neighbors or employees during a winter storm. Prepare your home and vehicle if you drive.

Home preparations

Supplies

- Include winter specific items to your emergency 'go-kit' supplies, such as rock salt, sand and other snow removal equipment.
- In case the electricity is cut off, make sure that you have sufficient heating fuel, emergency heating equipment, extra blankets, batteries and flashlights.
- Keep fire extinguishers on hand and make sure everyone in your house knows how to use them, especially if making house fires.

Protect home structures

- Install storm windows or cover windows with plastic.
- Insulate walls and attics and apply caulk and weather-stripping to doors and windows.
- Winterize your house, barn, shed or any other structure that may provide shelter for your family, neighbors, livestock or equipment.
- Clear rain gutters, repair roof leaks and cut away tree branches that could fall on a house or other structure during a storm.
- Hire a contractor to check the structural ability of the roof to sustain unusually heavy weight from the accumulation of snow or water, if drains on flat roofs do not work.

Preventing pipes from freezing

- Wrap pipes in insulation or layers of old newspapers.
- Cover the newspapers with plastic to keep out moisture.
- Let faucets drip a little to avoid freezing.
- Know how to shut off water valves.

State of Vermont, Orange County. A mixed spruce hardwood stands where 90 percent of the hardwood trees have broken tops or branches as a result of the an ice storm. Courtesy of Vermont Department of Forests, Parks and Recreation 2003/0564510

Vehicle preparations

- Keep in your vehicle a shovel, windshield scraper, extra hats and mittens, blanket, tow chain or rope, road salt and sand.
- Keep vehicles fueled and in good repair.
- Winterize your car by checking your car battery, ignition system, thermostat, lights, flashers, exhaust, heater, brakes, defroster and tires.
- Ensure there is adequate antifreeze, windshield washer fluid and oil and check regularly throughout the season.
- Avoid driving during a Winter Storm Warning or Blizzard Warning. If traveling by car during a Winter Weather Advisory or Winter Storm Watch, do so in daylight. Keep others informed of your schedule and route and stay on main roads. Avoid traveling alone.

During a winter storm

If inside

Maintain ventilation when using kerosene heaters to avoid a build-up of toxic fumes and always refuel outside. Keep all heaters at least three feet from flammable objects.

- Do not leave.
- Dress in several layers of loose fitting, light weight, warm clothing instead of one layer of heavy clothing.
- Maintain ventilation when using kerosene heaters to avoid a build-up of toxic fumes and always refuel outside. Keep all heaters at least three feet from flammable objects.
- Conserve fuel. Lower the thermostat to 65 degrees during the day and 55 degrees at night. Close off unused rooms.
- If the pipes freeze, remove any insulation or layers of newspapers and wrap pipes in rags. Completely open all faucets and pour hot water over the pipes, starting where they were most exposed to the cold or where the cold was most likely to seep in.
- Listen for news updates on road conditions, food availability and weather changes.

If outside

If outside, wear loose-fitting, layered, light-weight clothing. Layers can be removed to prevent perspiration and chill. Outer garments should be tightly woven and water repellent. Mittens are warmer than gloves because fingers generate warmth when they touch each other.

- Wear loose-fitting, layered, light-weight clothing. Layers can be removed to prevent perspiration and chill. Outer garments should be tightly woven and water repellent. Mittens are warmer than gloves because fingers generate warmth when they touch each other.
- Cover your mouth. Protect your lungs from extremely cold air by covering your mouth when outdoors. Try not to speak unless absolutely necessary.
- If shoveling snow, do few stretching exercises before starting and take frequent breaks.
- Avoid overexertion. Cold weather adds strain to the heart. Unaccustomed exercise, such as shoveling snow or pushing a car, can

bring on a heart attack or make other medical conditions worse. Be aware of symptoms of dehydration.

- Keep dry. Change wet clothing frequently to prevent a loss of body heat. Wet clothing loses all of its insulating value and transmits heat rapidly.

After a winter storm

- Remember to help your neighbors who may require special assistance, such as the elderly, people with infants or disabilities.
- Remove ice and snow from tree limbs, roof and other structures after the storm passes.
- Watch for signs of frostbite and hypothermia.

Frostbite and hypothermia

Frostbite is a serious condition whereby your body is reacting to having its temperature go below 90 degrees Fahrenheit. It can cause permanent damage and even require amputation.

Symptoms

- Loss of feeling and a white or pale appearance in fingers, toes or nose and ear lobes
- Uncontrollable shivering
- Slow speech
- Memory lapses
- Frequent stumbling
- Drowsiness
- Exhaustion

Treatment

- Begin warming the person slowly and around their waist first. Use your own body heat to help.
- Seek immediate medical assistance.
- Arms and legs should be warmed last because stimulation of the limbs can drive cold blood toward the heart and lead to heart failure.
- Put the person in dry clothing and wrap their entire body in a blanket.
- Never give a frostbite or hypothermia victim alcohol or caffeine as in coffee or tea. Depressants and stimulants can cause irregular heart beats that increases the damage from hypothermia.

Vehicle CO Poisoning

During the Blizzard of 1996, the Centers for Disease Control and Prevention received reports that dozens of children and elderly people in the Northeast suffered from carbon monoxide (CO) poisoning while warming from the cold in idling vehicles. Because snow either filled or covered the vehicle exhaust pipes, CO fumes seeped inside poisoning the occupants. To avoid vehicle CO poisoning:

· ▪ Make sure the tail pipe is clear before starting the engine.
▪ Leave windows open whenever the car is idling.
▪ Do not leave anyone in a parked vehicle with the engine running while shoveling snow.

Hazardous substances in the home

Your home and the products you use can give off or contain toxic and/or flammable materials. For example, sources of heat, such as furnaces or stoves, can give off the poisonous gas carbon monoxide. Cleaning products for your clothes, home and car or finishing materials for varnishing or painting can be harmful to your health if inhaled, swallowed, splashed in your eye or located near a source of heat/fire.

Poisonous gas in the home: carbon monoxide

Carbon monoxide (CO) is a poisonous gas that is odorless, tasteless, invisible and heavier than air. According to the Centers for Disease Control and Prevention (CDC), more than 500 Americans die from unintentional carbon monoxide poisoning per year and more than 2,000 intentionally poison themselves to commit suicide.

People and animals can die from inhaling CO that builds up slowly in the home or quickly through an excessive use of items that produce CO in an enclosed space. Those more susceptible to CO poisoning are unborn babies, infants and people with chronic heart disease, anemia or respiratory problems. The following can produce dangerous amounts of CO: furnaces, hot water heaters, fire places stoves, lanterns, burning charcoal and wood, and gas ranges and heating systems, small gasoline engines, cars and trucks.

Symptoms of carbon monoxide poisoning

When unsuspected, CO poisoning can be difficult to diagnose because the symptoms are similar to other illnesses. Sleeping or intoxicated people can die from carbon monoxide poisoning before experiencing any of the following symptoms.

- Headache
- Dizziness
- Weakness
- Nausea
- Vomiting
- Chest pain
- Confusion
- Loss of consciousness

Preventing carbon monoxide poisoning

Protect yourself from CO poisoning by placing alarms in low-lying areas around items that produce CO. They should be placed on each level of your home and in your bedroom(s). Check the batteries and the shelf life of CO detectors and use them in pairs. Sensors can sometimes burn out and give false readings. The CDC suggests the following ways to use and check if fuel-burning items work properly.

Make sure appliances work properly

- Ensure that all fuel-burning appliances are properly installed, maintained and operated.
- Have a professional inspect furnaces, water heaters, and gas dryers annually.
- Clean and check fireplace chimneys and flues annually.
- Inspect vehicle exhaust systems routinely for defects and and/or snow during the wintertime.

Use heaters and vehicles correctly

- Never leave unvented fuel-burning space heaters unattended or without open doors or windows in the room to provide fresh air.
- Never use a gas range or oven to heat a home.
- Never use a charcoal grill, hibachi, lantern or portable camping stove inside a home, tent or camper.
- Unless the equipment is professionally installed and vented, never run a generator, pressure washer or any gasoline-powered engine. Never use them inside a basement, garage, or other enclosed structure — even if the doors or windows are open.
- Never run a motor vehicle, generator, pressure washer or any gasoline-powered engine outside of an open window or door where exhaust can vent into an enclosed area.
- Never leave the motor running in a vehicle parked in an enclosed or semi-enclosed space, such as a closed garage.

Chemical household products

A variety of consumer cleaning and finishing products can cause digestive, respiratory, skin and eye problems if incorrectly used, stored or disposed. Simple steps can prevent a hazardous materials (HazMat) incident from happening in your home. Before using chemical materials in the home, always read the directions. Never smoke near chemicals or use them near an open flame. FEMA and the American Red Cross suggest the following storage and disposal tips.

A variety of consumer cleaning and finishing products can cause digestive, respiratory, skin and eye problems if incorrectly used, stored or disposed.

L.I.E.S.

Key ways to prevent chemical accidents in the home can be used by remembering LIES:

- **L**imit the amount of HazMat you store.
- **I**solate products in safe containers and enclosed areas away from heat sources and children.
- **E**liminate products you no longer need or that are nearly empty.
- **S**eparate materials as indicated on the bottle; for example, chlorine bleach should not be near ammonia.

To avoid polluting the inside and outside of your home, follow specific disposal instructions for different types of hazardous materials.

Throwing away chemical bottles

To avoid polluting the inside and outside of your home, follow specific disposal instructions for different types of hazardous materials. There may be a few options for one type of material.

Down the drain

Before putting any of the following chemical containers in the trash or recycling bin, empty the last bits of the material down the drain with plenty of water to dilute it.

- Vehicle anti-freeze
- Fertilizer
- Household disinfectant
- Laundry and dish washing detergent
- Cleaning solutions: rug and upholstery, toilet bowl, bathroom and glass and drain
- Bleach
- Rubbing alcohol
- Medicine

Using newspaper and plastic in the trash

Once finished with the following materials, wrap them in newspaper and in a plastic bag before disposing.

- Car items: brake fluid
- Cleaning solutions: toilet bowl, drain, oven and those in powder form
- Polish: car, furniture, floor, nail
- Finishing: paint thinners and strippers, water-based paint, wood preserves
- Outdoors: pesticides, fertilizer, insect repellent
- Detergent: dish and laundry soaps

At recycling or collection sites

The following can be discarded at specific recycling and/or collection sites.

- Kerosene
- Diesel fuel
- Car items: Motor or fuel oil, batteries or battery acid, transmission fluid, tires, power-steering fluid
- Gun cleaning solvents
- Paint: large amounts, thinner or stripper
- Empty spray cans

Spilled chemicals

If you spill chemicals, clean them up using plastic gloves and rags. Dry the rags outside before wrapping them in a sealed plastic bag to put in the garbage can. Wash any exposed areas and throw away any contaminated clothes. Dispose of the container accordingly.

Response to a home chemical emergency

Quick response to a chemical incident is key to limiting pain and damage. The following are steps to follow if chemicals are swallowed, go in the eyes or cause a fire or explosion.

If chemicals are swallowed

- Find the containers immediately to have information ready for medical professionals or dispatchers.
- Call poison control immediately at 1-800-222-1222, 911 or use a phone number from your local emergency management agency.
- Follow the poison control operator's directions carefully.

If chemicals go in the eye(s)

- Follow the instructions on the container.
- Continue to flush out the eye(s) even if the pain goes away.
- Seek medical attention to check for damage and if all of the poison was washed out.

In the event of fire or explosion

- Evacuate your home immediately.
- Move UPWIND, UPHILL and as far away as possible.
- Call fire services from a safe distance.

After a home chemical emergency

Immediately wash all exposed areas of the body with lots of water and soap. Areas still contaminated may burn or irritate the skin. Throw away the contaminated clothes in a plastic bag.

If there is a chemical burn

- Call 911.
- Remove clothing and jewelry around the area.
- Pour clean, cool water over the burn for 15 to 30 minutes.
- Loosely cover the burn with clean, sterile dressing, such as gauze, that does NOT stick to the burn.
- Follow-up with medical help as soon as possible.

If you swallow a chemical, immediately call poison control at 1-800-222-1222, 911 or through a local number from your local emergency management agency.

Fires that occur in apartment buildings can quickly spread. Make sure your fire alarms are always working and plan and practice evacuation routes.
2003/0564506

Wild fires can devastate communities and take people by surprise if they do not plan.
2003/0564507

Fires

Small and large fires can occur in virtually any setting — your home, your office, your vehicles, public transportation or even in the idyllic setting of a national park. Create a fire evacuation plan with so that there are two ways to exit a room. Make sure fire alarms have charged batteries and are working properly. If at work, keep an office plan noting fire escapes and exits in the event you may need to evacuate. If you look around your home, you will most likely notice several real fire hazards, such as open or exposed hazardous materials containers or excessive clutter. Fires cause two main health dangers: burns and smoke inhalation. Smoke inhalation causes small particles in smoke to become lodged in the lungs, further causing permanent respiratory damage that can be fatal.

Using fire extinguishers

Fires ignited from oil, grease or electricity require different types of extinguishers. Using the wrong type of extinguisher can prove disastrous. Explain your preparations to the hardware store sales staff and make sure you buy the right equipment for your needs.

Structural fires

Contact your local fire department for information on responding to structural fires before they occur. Fire fighters are the experts and can help you with questions about your specific situation.

While homeowners or business employees can effectively extinguish some fires, do not assume that you can put out fires by yourself. If the fire is contained and small, put out the fire. If the fire is large and out of control, move out of harms way and call the emergency authorities to report the details.

Vehicle fires

In the event you are in or near a vehicle that catches fire, you and any other occupants should immediately exit the vehicle or the area. Vehicles are smaller and more confined than buildings thus it is more important to exit as fast as possible — particularly because of the likely presence of explosive gasoline or diesel fuel. When you have exited the vehicle, move as far away as possible to avoid injury from burning or exploding fuel.

Wildfires

If you encounter a wildfire, evacuate the area as quickly as possible. People have had to pack and evacuate their homes within as short of a period time as 15 minutes to survive wild fires. Be sure to follow directions from your local authorities, or, if none are available, immediately begin moving away from the fire.

If possible, determine the direction in which the fire is moving and move at right angles to this direction and away from the fire. Be prepared to keep moving from one evacuation point to another in the event the fire continues to spread. This is why it is essential to have your emergency 'go-kit' and a vehicle or other available mode of transportation ready to evacuate possibly for days or months depending on damage. The impact of wild fires may cause flight delays, temporary closures of highways and bridges and electricity outages.

If you don't have to evacuate but your home is in the general area of a wildfire, stay indoors. This is especially necessary for children, the elderly and people with heart and lung problems. Exercise inside to avoid smoke inhalation.

A power outage can last a few moments up to a few days. Make sure you have non-perishable food, water, flashlights, radio and batteries. 2003/0564509

Power outage

Most power outages don't become emergencies because they are usually corrected within a few hours; nevertheless it is important to respond calmly and efficiently when one occurs.

Since cordless phones do not work during power outages, have a regular phone in the home.

- Make sure you have your supplies stocked: water, non-perishable food, flashlights, radio and batteries.
- Since cordless phones do not work during power outages, have a regular phone in the home.
- Use flashlights instead of candles to avoid fire accidents.
- Look for secondary emergencies: the interruption of essential services or other life-saving measures including ongoing medical support.
- Check for emergencies related to the unexpected resumption of service. If you are concerned with secondary emergencies, turn off utilities during the outage. Have professionals turn them back on to restore service.
- Report the outage to the company that provides the service. Even if the outage seems to be widespread, don't assume that someone else will report the problem for you.

Public transportation emergencies

The number and types of transportation emergencies vary widely. They range from minor subway train schedule interruptions to major airline crashes or train derailments. It is highly unlikely that you will ever be involved in a dangerous or life-threatening emergency while you are using public transportation. If you ever find yourself in this situation, however, there are a few important things to consider.

Civil disturbance can cause lives and millions of dollars in damage. 2003/0564511

Los Angeles Riots

A civil disturbance can occur instantaneously and wreak havoc on an entire community. "On April 29, 1992, a Los Angeles jury found two LA police officers not guilty of police brutality towards Rodney King on all counts. This included: official misconduct, excessive force, filing false police reports and assault with a deadly weapon after alleged beating," recounts Marleen Wong, Director of Crisis Counseling and Intervention Services in Los Angeles Unified School District. "This was all captured on videotape. In response to the decision as well as on-going police brutality and rioting, widespread arson and looting took place across downtown, Southeast and South Central Los Angeles. Local media helicopters provided constant coverage of the looting and areas lacking police presence.

The next day, the mayor declared a local state of emergency and all schools in the southern part of Los Angeles were closed. The California governor's office sent more than 2,000 National Guard soldiers to stop the chaos. Some merchants stood on rooftops with guns and automatic weapons. Senseless violence seemed to compound itself. Although more reinforcements were sent by the third day, the incident resulted in 50 people killed, thousands injured, more than 3,000 people arrested, hundreds of businesses looted and $1 billion in property damages."

Preventive safety tips

- As you enter the vehicle — whether an airplane, train, bus, subway train, ferry or cruise ship — take a few moments to review your emergency options. These moments of familiarization could give you time to react to a crisis.
- Read over the emergency response posters.
- Locate the emergency exits.
- Locate the fire estinguishers which are many times under the seats near emergency exits.
- Know what staff will give you guidance and direction should a problem occur.

Responding to a transportation incident

As soon as possible, locate an intercom or a staff member to inform them of key details: the problem, time it occurred, amount of people in your enclosed area and any other related information.

Be aware that you may have to act on your own if the transportation authorities are unable to provide guidance or assistance. There could be circumstances under which transit authority personnel are themselves victims of an incident.

It is critical during a public transportation emergency that you stay calm. Typically other passengers will share your vehicle. In crisis situations, others will show stress and your calm behavior could help others remain calm as well.

Civil disturbances

Civil unrest has many causes. Some examples include: festering tensions between neighboring communities, a political event sparking anger from the general public or a particular group, the stress and confusion from major disasters and unrest at an entertainment venue. Civil unrest at entertainment venues is worsened by poor event planning and control. It can spill over into nearby areas businesses and residential areas. Sometimes the authorities will be able to block off the area(s) affected but other times the unrest may occur in several, scattered areas at once.

Response to a civil disturbance

During times of civil disturbance, misinformation can fuel rumors and affect the chain reaction of events. Therefore, take care when making decisions to leave or stay.

- Whenever possible, avoid contact with the rioters and keep a low profile.
- Listen for the authorities to announce if you should shelter-in-place or evacuate the area.
- If you must vacate your home, make sure you secure any important personal documentation as explained in *Chapter 3: Personal Disaster Preparedness*. Find a place to stay (with friends or family) away from the affected areas.
- Do what you can to protect property. Lock doors and windows and take valuables with you. Do not risk your life for your possessions.
- If evacuating by car, do not try to drive through a crowd.
- If you are confronted with a group of angry people causing damage to other people or places, leave the area as soon as possible. If you confront the rioters you may risk injury to yourself.

Use of personal firearms

Using firearms provides limited protection against an angry mob because they may also be armed. In addition, actions of a mob are unpredictable and people may rush towards you in an attempt to disarm you.

Keeping a firearm on hand for protection is a personal decision. If you do decide to keep a firearm to deter rioters, use it only when threatened with deadly force. In all cases, the safest course is to avoid open confrontation with rioters and leave the job of civil defense to the police and National Guard.

Quiz yourself, family and your friends

1. A Hurricane Watch is issued when:

    A. A Hurricane forms.

    B. Officials at NOAA decide to issue a Hurricane Watch.

    C. When there is a tropical storm.

    D. When Hurricane conditions are possible within 48 hours.

2. The best place to take shelter in the event of a tornado is:

    A. A room on the second story

    B. Outside in the tool shed

    C. In a corn field

    D. In a ditch

    E. In a basement or storm cellar

3. If the authorities issue a mandatory evacuation order in the event of a flood you should:

    A. Wait until flood waters subside.

    B. Go swimming.

    C. Leave for higher ground immediately.

    D. Begin preparations.

4. When confronted with a wildfire it is best to:

    A. Seek shelter beneath a rock or outcropping.

    B. Move away from the blaze at right angles to its direction of movement.

    C. Run away from the blaze.

    D. Dive into a pond of water.

5. What part of a hurricane causes the most number of lives to be lost?

    A. Wind

    B. Waves

    C. The Storm Surge

    D. Rain

Find out the answers to the Chapter 8 quiz on page 201.

There is a greater health risk in your community from hazardous materials accidents than the use of Weapons of Mass Destruction. 2003/0564514

Part Three **Chapter 9**

Hazardous Materials and Weapons of Mass Destruction

"I told my husband, 'if you're going to be stubborn, stay here [at home]. But I have to make sure these kids get to safety'," said Lisa Perkins. *She was trying to convince her husband to evacuate with their four children, their pet Chihuahua and 3,000 other citizens because a derailed train carrying 10,600 gallons of liquid sulfuric acid released a cloud of hazardous materials near their town Farragut, Tennessee on September 15, 2002.*

While there has been much talk about Weapons of Mass Destruction, those same elements in hazardous materials transported past your home presents a more likely risk.

"Tenn. Derailment Forces Evacuations,"
Associated Press, September 16, 2002

Introduction

After the September 11 attacks, Weapons of Mass Destruction (WMD) became a household word in America. The question on everyone's mind: If Al-Qaeda could pull off that attack, could they use even more devastating weapons? The anthrax attacks in October of 2001 certainly indicated that biological terrorism was possible. Videotapes obtained during the invasion of Afghanistan seem to indicate experiments with chemical agents were tested for their effectiveness. The June 2002 US Department of Justice announcement of the arrest of a suspected al-Qaeda member who allegedly planned to detonate a radiological dispersal device, or dirty bomb, in Washington DC, raised public fear of the use of radiological weapons.

Much has been written about WMD over the years, especially of nuclear holocaust during the Cold War, and many people feel helpless when faced with the threat of these weapons. In looking at terrorist WMD incidents realistically, you can certainly see straightforward and practical ways to protect yourself from harm — without using expensive equipment.

Chapter Overview

This chapter will give you a realistic look at the risks of HazMat and WMD as well as a range of practical actions you can take in the event of a suspected or real incident.

- Hazardous materials (HazMat) in your community
- Organizations handling HazMat
- Symptoms of agents
- Self-protection measures
- Treatment

Find out how companies handle hazardous materials near your home. 2003/0564514

Knowing The Facts

Check the facts when a hazardous material spill occurs, especially in your community. US Coast Guard (USCG) Commander James McPherson, Chief of Public Affairs, explains, "the US Coast Guard needed to spend a great deal of time discussing who was in charge of joint information center (JIC.) [A JIC is created when organizations speak to the press at the same time many times during an emergency.] At a major oil spill, private industry attempted to use the JIC credibility to put out information favorable and inaccurate to the industry. A representative from an oil company attempted to change the information the JIC was going to release to indicate that the source of the thousands of gallons of spilled oil was not yet determined. The USCG confirmed immediately that the 20-foot hole in their oil tanker was the source. The oil company's behavior threatened the accuracy of the information to the public, its credibility for possible investigations and further dealings with the authorities."

Source: *Jane's Crisis Communications Handbook (2003)*

In daily life, hazardous materials (HazMat) accidents that a family like the Perkins faced on a sleepy Sunday night has a greater chance of occurring with the same health and environmental impact. Tens of thousands of organizations and transportation companies handle HazMat on a daily basis. The National Resource Center of the US Coast Guard receives up to 30,000 notifications of industrial chemical spills per year.

Hazardous materials in your community

HazMat consists of chemical materials that potentially pose a risk to your life, health, property and the environment if they are released or used improperly. An industrial chemical incident can happen anywhere particularly since a variety of land, sea and air carriers transport HazMat as cargo. Chemical spills and other releases, such as methane gas and groundwater contamination, can indeed happen anywhere. The Federal Emergency Management Agency (FEMA) created the following HazMat risks information for citizen's participating in the Community Emergency Response Teams (CERT).

Organizations that manage or create HazMat include:

- Chemical plants
- Local automotive and gas service stations
- Hospitals
- HazMat waste sites (up to 30,000)
- Transport vehicles

Identify HazMat risks

Many communities have Local Emergency Planning Committees (LEPC) that identify industrial hazardous materials and inform the public on potential risks. Citizens can participate in LEPC groups to offer their ideas on community safety. Companies that have hazardous materials are supposed to provide annual reports to LEPC. To find out how close you are to facilities that produce, store or transport HazMat and/or waste, call your local emergency management agency to find out if there is a LEPC in your area.

Response to a large HazMat release

A chemical release from a HazMat accident or radiation release from a nuclear plant accident can cause the same effect to your health and the environment as the use of Weapons of Mass Destruction (WMD). See symptoms of chemical exposure on 149. For radiation exposure symptoms, see page 150. Self-protection measures for chemical and radiation exposure see the seven self-protection responses on page 152.

Weapons of Mass Destruction (WMD)

The term WMD has been used for many years and is most often associated with chemical, biological, radiological and nuclear weapons (CBRN). In a military context, WMD is used for large-scale and overt events, such the allied forces and German military use of mustard gas in World War I, the US nuclear bombing of Hiroshima and Nagasaki at the end of World War II and the Iraqi government chemical bombing of Kurdish civilians in 1988.

Farragut, TN, September 15, 2002 — A hazardous material worker responds to 24 derailed Norfolk Southern Railways train cars releasing 10,600 gallons of sulfuric acid. Source: Associated Press. 2003/0564512

Terrorists, however, are thought to have not yet developed these weapons to full potential and certainly do not have a stockpile of them equivalent to large military forces. When terrorist groups have used CBR, it has thus far resulted in mass disruption of the areas targeted rather than mass destruction of people and places. In turn, CBRN risks include a wide range of hazards and possible consequences, from a few to hundreds of people becoming sick. For example, while the October 2001 Anthrax attacks created widespread fear, especially in the New York City and Washington, DC metropolitan areas, a total of 5 fatalities and 22 injured resulted.

Danger of WMD agents

Great differences exist between the various CBRN agents. Some pose fatal dangers within hours to days and others can create long-term health problems. Some, but not all, chemical agents can incapacitate and kill within seconds. The resulting gas may dissipate to safe levels in a matter of minutes or hours. Biological exposure would result in symptoms possibly within hours or days. Without effective decontamination, some bio-hazards could continue to pose a threat for many years. Radiological weapons can have immediate impacts or long-term effects depending on whether they are used to pollute an area or are used in a bomb. Nuclear weapons use is highly unlikely but if used they would cause fires, blast damage, mass casualties and long-term radiation. See *Chapter 12: Appendices* for additional background on CBRN weapons use and characteristics.

CBRN weapons delivery

CBRN materials can be delivered in different ways. **Chemical weapons** are not easy to use because a variety of uncontrollable weather conditions and terrain affect the range of chemicals and the level of concentration. Temperature, humidity, precipitation, wind speed as well as surrounding buildings and land all have to be perfect for chemical weapons to harm you.

Biological weapons can be released in the open air or spread by a person purposely infected with the disease. If released in the open air, biological weapons depend on a variety of specific weather conditions. Like chemical weapons, these include: temperature, humidity, precipitation, wind speed

HazMat in Your Backyard

"For a few weeks this fall, I ran threat and vulnerability studies on a variety of security issues throughout New York state counties," said LTC Robert Domenici., Program Coordinator of Homeland Security Exercise and Evaluation, New York State WMD Task Force. "For the most part, local officials knew the threats and vulnerabilities in their own communities, but knew little about neighboring counties or hazards transported through their counties. Hazardous materials are increasingly being transported on our roads, railways and in our airspace. These hazardous materials, if exposed, will stretch the capability of most local agencies and recourses to respond. Local agencies need to conduct threat and vulnerability assessments annually to see how

False Incident

The impact of false WMD incidents cannot be underestimated. Louie Fernandez, Senior Bureau Chief of Public Affairs for Miami-Dade Fire Rescue and Office of Emergency Management recounts: "On August 21, 2002, several people were reported to be coughing, sneezing and having difficulty breathing at a security checkpoint at Miami International Airport. Even though the Miami-Dade Fire Rescue public information officer arrived at the airport 11 minutes after the report, rumors were rampant and local, national and international broadcast reporters were on-air live outside the terminal. The incident was probably due to a discarded pepper spray can going off in the trash and not the original speculation of anthrax, fueling the intense press response." Staying calm before authorities confirm suspicious item is dangerous is key to avoiding panic and over-reaction.

and level of sunlight. If an attack were to make an impact, a target would most likely be in an enclosed area, such as in buildings, subways or tunnels — which would require you to evacuate — not shelter-in-place.

Radiological devices are more of a means of causing mass disruption (fear, panic, psychological trauma) than a true weapon of mass destruction (large numbers of casualties and destroyed buildings). This does not mean, however, that the disruptive impact is not just as important as destructive effects. The limited delivery area of most devices means the radiation would not kill large numbers of people. While the conventional bomb used in dirty bombs could cause casualties and structural damage, radiological experts believe most dirty bombs would not generate immediate radiation-related deaths.

Regarding **nuclear weapons**, it is important to note that it is very, very, unlikely that a nuclear explosion would occur. Major national and international efforts are in place to control the weapons and materials that could be used to create such an explosion. So why include this kind of information? The impact of such an event, in the extremely rare and unlikely case that it could occur, would affect a very large number of people. Because a danger exists, however slight, that a nuclear explosion could happen it is important to include this kind of information.

False incidents and hoaxes

In the short-term, false incidents and hoaxes may cause significant concern and disruption if not dealt with properly. A **false incident** happens when an object is suspected or mistakenly thought to be a CBRN weapon. A **hoax** can be either a threat — possibly by telephone, email, mail or a fake object appearing to be the 'real thing.' Police, bomb-squad or fire department personnel confirm hoaxes. If a hoax cannot be readily confirmed, it is classed as **suspicious**. Those found responsible for hoaxes can face legal consequences, similar as with people who sent false anthrax letters during the October 2001 anthrax attacks.

Clear (overt) releases

In general terms, agents can be delivered in clear or hidden ways. A clear or overt method is when witnesses and/or first responders know that something has happened. This may or may not include other details, such as why, how or where. For instance, one overt method would be an explosion with certain known details, such as, location, time, casualties, hazards used and other known factors. Another overt method, though less clear, would be people suddenly and simultaneously becoming ill with the same symptoms but at different locations. Something has happened, but it is possible that responders do not know the cause or intent.

Hidden (covert) releases

There are some chemical, biological and radiological (CBR) hazards that have a delayed onset of symptoms. These hazards can complicate first response because the occurrence and/or source of the attack is difficult to find. Covert releases can happen along with a variety of other 'unknowns.' For instance, the community may not even know something has occurred, especially if the symptoms are delayed over time. Or, the community may know an incident has occurred but wrongly identifies the cause. Sometimes people will discover CBR materials but not know that they are dangerous until symptoms appear. In the case of the anthrax letters, emergency officials were not aware of the significance of strange powder being delivered through the postal service until people started to become ill and die.

Symptoms of chemical, biological and radiological release

Because the effects of nuclear devices are of a different magnitude than CBR hazards, the following sections deal with CBR threats. There is a role for nuclear preparedness; the *Nuclear events* section on page 157 provides self-protection options to consider in the rare event of a nuclear explosion. CBR hazards, however, are more likely to cause symptoms among unprotected people quickly. In the case of an accidental HazMat release or WMD attack, authorities will most likely issue warnings through the media.

> Because the effects of nuclear devices are of a different magnitude from chemical, biological and radiological hazards (CBR), the following sections deals with CBR threats.

Symptoms of a chemical release

Some symptoms of a chemical incident could become more likely than others.

Likely

- **Sudden onset of symptoms**
    - Small pupils, cough, shortness of breath
    - Sweating, vomiting
    - Convulsions, breathing stops
    - Black out/loss of consciousness
    - Redness of skin, blisters, eye irritation

- **Unexplained victims**
    - Multiple victims
    - Victims concentrated in a given area

- **Dead or dying animals**
    - Lack of insects

Less likely

- **Visual indicators**
  - Unusual liquid, spray or vapor
  - Droplets, oily film
  - Unexplained odor (This may or may not be distinguishable from background odors.)
  - Low flying clouds/fog unrelated to weather

- **Other indicators**
  - Unusual metal debris (This could possibly be part of a weapon's device or other mechanism.)

Symptoms of a biological release

Delayed symptoms of illness are many times the first signs of exposure to a biological agent. Symptoms can take days or even weeks to appear. In addition, the victim is most likely unaware of exposure. Recognizing dangerous biological substances would include noticing and reporting a suspicious activities or items before symptoms appear would be ideal but not always possible.

- **Unusual casualties**
  - Unusual illness for region/area
  - Definite pattern inconsistent with natural diseases

- **Unusual liquid, spray, vapor or powder**
  - Spraying and suspicious devices or packages
  - Parcels containing strange powder

- **Unusual dead or dying animals**
  - Sick or dying animals, people or fish

- **Unusual swarms of insects**

Symptoms of radiological release

The first indicator of an attack with a 'dirty bomb' would be the detonation of a bomb. First responders would confirm if the attack included radiological materials through routine testing and possible eye witness and/or victims' reports of suspicious activity or item, or, in the worse case, radiological symptoms.

A radiological device can use a solid contaminant, a small group of particles or loose material. If large quantities are released, some of the following indicators may appear.

Recognizing dangerous biological substances, would include noticing and reporting suspicious activities or items before symptoms appear would be ideal but not always possible.

The first indicator of an attack with a 'dirty bomb' would be the detonation of a bomb.

- **Unexplained casualties**
  - Multiple victims
  - Illness from an unexplained source: nausea, vomiting, diarrhea, fatigue, skin-reddening, dehydration
  - Victims concentrated in a given region

- **Strange devices/packages**
  - Containers with radiation symbols
  - Unusual debris
  - Heat emission
  - Contents glowing in low light conditions

Protecting yourself during a CBRN emergency

Whether a HazMat accident or intentional violence, if you are near a suspected release of CBRN materials, you have three options: evacuate, remain indoors (shelter-in-place) or seek shelter nearby. Depending on the situation, one of these choices will be optimal. These actions can protect you from short and long-term physical affects. You can choose to buy protective equipment, but taking quick action by moving away from the point of the release will help you the most.

This section is divided into two sets of response directions: 1) for chemical, biological and radiological (CBR) incidents and 2) for nuclear explosions (not to be confused with nuclear plant accidents, which are classified as radiological releases). While different in origin, CBR agents require similar responses for a HazMat accident and an intentional act of violence. A nuclear blast requires different ways to protect yourself and if used correctly, can save your life and prevent long-term damage from radiation following a blast.

Chemical, biological and radiological incidents

What you decide to do during a CBR incident will greatly affect your risks of having the material touch you or your clothes (called contamination) and spreading it to others. Although unlikely, it is possible, that emergency responders will not arrive at an incident scene quickly. If you are in immediate danger consider the following procedures to protect and decontaminate yourself after a CBR release.

NOTE: In all cases, defer to professional responders once they have arrived. These guidelines should not replace special training and instruction on handling CBR exposure. This information is only intended as a life-saving stop-gap until medical personnel can treat you.

Cause for Delayed Emergency Services

In the case of a chemical incident, there is a slight chance that responders may be, at least initially, overwhelmed or become victims themselves. In other cases, terrorists may have directly targeted responders or access to the incident scene may be blocked. Understanding how to protect yourself while evacuating, sheltering-in-place or seeking a shelter can shield you from danger.

While different in origin, chemical, biological or radiological (CBR) agents require similar responses for a HazMat accident and an intentional act of violence.

Seven self-protection responses

If a CBR release is known or suspected based on recognized signs and symptoms, consider the following **quick reference** to help you protect yourself.

1. **Remain calm:** beware of panic from your own fear and the fear of others.
2. **Cover mouth, nose and skin:** block exposure with available protection (wet scarf, mask). If contact hazard is suspected, cover exposed skin.
3. **Move away from the source of the agent release to a safe area:** decide to either a) evacuate the building or area UPHILL and UPWIND, b) shelter-in-place above ground or c) seek nearby shelter.
4. **Stay away from the general population:** contact with other persons may place them or yourself at risk of contamination.
5. **Contact emergency response personnel (police, fire, medical, National Guard):** once you are safely away from the contaminated areas, wait for emergency responders for 15 minutes then continue to evacuate.
6. **Beware of delayed effects:** some chemical and most biological and radiological agents take effect over a long period of time.
7. **Help others:** calm other victims who are scared.

Possible CBR situations and responses

The following are situations involving a CBR release that require you to make an immediate decision to evacuate, remain in-place or seek shelter elsewhere. Start planning to seek help on your own if there is no sight or sound of emergency services arriving within 15 minutes.

- **You 'think' an agent is present but there are no victims:** move away from the scene but do not leave the immediate area. For example, in an office, leave the room, close the door behind you but stay inside the building. Leaving the building will risk spreading potential contamination to others and actually *delay your medical treatment*.

- **You see a dangerous/suspicious device but nothing has yet happened:** evacuate and contact the emergency services. The minimum recommended evacuation distance is at least 300 feet. Ideally, evacuate UPWIND and, if possible, UPHILL.

- **You know an agent is released but there are no victims:** Evacuate and contact emergency services. Do not go near others to avoid contamination either from you or them.

- **Agent is in the air and you are outside:** People who may have been contaminated should follow the directions prescribed in the seven self-protection responses on page 152. Anyone not exposed should move at least 300 feet away, UPWIND and UPHILL of the possible hazard. If you are already down wind, move CROSSWIND which is perpendicular (90 degrees) to the direction of the wind.

- **Agent is in a building with only some people contaminated/affected:** if you are contaminated, evacuate the building and follow the seven self-protection responses on page 152 People not exposed should evacuate and move at least 300 feet away, UPWIND and UPHILL of the possible hazard. If you are already down wind — move CROSSWIND.

- **Agent is in the air and you can see victims:** if people are in obvious distress, move to a safer location. Follow the seven self-protection responses on page 152. If inside a contaminated building, move outside into fresh air. If outside, move away from those affected, ideally UPWIND and UPHILL or seek shelter nearby. Shut the windows and doors and turn off the ventilation system.

Radiation considerations

In addition to using the seven self-protection responses, you can take extra steps to reduce or prevent radiation exposure. Unlike chemical hazards, which may dissipate naturally — through the effects of wind and weather — radiation will pose a significant risk until the source is removed. If a radiation hazard is suspected, take four critical actions:

1. **Time:** reduce the duration of exposure.
2. **Distance:** increase distance from the radiation source.
3. **Shielding:** place shielding between yourself and the source.
4. **Quantity:** limit the quantity of radiation. (For example, decontaminate yourself and/or move away from the source of danger.)

Use of sealed rooms

Public mention of sealed rooms greatly increased after the US Department of Homeland Security advised Americans to buy duct tape and plastic sheeting to seal a room. Opinions vary on the usefulness of sealed rooms. A variety of uncontrollable weather conditions have to be just right to allow chemical and biological releases to be harmful. If a train derailment released toxic levels of a chemical, the authorities may tell you to stay in the highest level of your house or apartment building, shut windows and turn off the

Shelter-in-place vs. Seeking Shelter

Shelter-in-place: If you are inside and a release happens outside nearby, you are safer staying where you are. Go to the highest floor, shut the windows and doors and turn off the ventilation system.

Seeking shelter: If you are outside fleeing a release, consider seeking shelter in a safe building nearby. Go to the highest floor, shut the windows and doors and turn off the ventilation system.

Whether you decide to shelter 'in-place' or into a building, you can go into an prepared sealed room for **temporary** protection.

ventilation system until further notice. After the chemicals settle and if the area affected is large, the authorities would give evacuation instructions while helping those in the most danger with special equipment. In this situation, you could also enter a prepared sealed room or a room without windows, such as a bathroom, with any openings covered with towels.

Knowing how to use a sealed room

If you decide it is sensible for you to prepare a sealed room, set aside a room ahead of time and understand how to use it for the very short time that it is useful.

If possible, call emergency services to inform them you are entering the room with the following information.

- Your location
- Air supply (See formula below.)
- Number of people
- Time entered and entrance sealed
- Time the seal must be broken to prevent suffocation
- If oxygen bottles or air filters are available, make note of how much additional time this allows.

If possible, stay abreast of emergency statements and information by radio, television or by phone.

How long can I stay in a sealed room?

Leave the sealed room before oxygen and carbon dioxide levels become dangerous. Generally, one person has 2 minutes worth of air per cubic foot of space in a room.

Sealed Room Air Supply Formula

$\underline{2 \times \text{length} \times \text{width} \times \text{height of room in feet}}$ = 'Safe' time limit (in minutes)
number of people in the room

Example of safe time limit in a sealed room

One room 10 feet wide, 10 feet long and 8 feet high:

- **One person** would have about 26 hours and 40 minutes of safe air.
- **Two people** in the same room would have about 13 hours and 20 minutes.
- **Three people** would have approximately 8 hours and 52 minutes.

While all incidents are different depending on the amount and delivery of the agents, weather conditions and surrounding areas (number of buildings and other terrain features), people **generally would need to stay in a sealed room from one to 10 hours to avoid contamination.** If possible, listen for an 'all clear' announcement from first responders before exiting.

How do I leave a sealed room?

Ideally, when you leave a sealed room, the agents have dispersed and you are at low risk of contamination. To plan for the worst-case scenario, when leaving the sealed room assume you are entering a contaminated environment. If you cannot contact first responders, start planning your exit an hour before the healthy air supply is gone.

Leaving a sealed room

1. Protect your airway with the best protection available (respirator, mask, wet cloth).
2. Protect your skin with the best protection available (clothing over entire body, such as a hood and gloves)
3. Do not touch surfaces unless it is necessary. Walk carefully so as not to disturb dust that may be coated with toxins.

Once outside

1. Move in the direction of the nearest hospital that is UPWIND and, if possible, UPHILL of the point of release. If you are downwind of the point of release, walk CROSSWIND.

2. Avoid physical contact with those you pass on the way to the hospital to prevent harming yourself or others.

3. Use an evacuation route that:
   - Leads away and moves UPHILL and UPWIND of the release.
   - Minimizes your exposure to other people.

Emergency decontamination

After notifying emergency services and waiting for their arrival, consider these basic guidelines to reduce or clean off the contaminant. If possible, move to an area that is at least 300 feet from the incident, UPWIND and preferably UPHILL. Given the size of an incident you may have to move further away from the site.

If contaminant is inhaled

1. Move to a safe location UPHILL and UPWIND, where possible in a breeze.
2. Wait for additional medical support. It may be helpful to lie on the ground with your head into the wind.

Droplets of liquid chemical agent are on the skin

The *brush and blot* method can be used to remove liquid chemical droplets from your skin.

1. **Move** to a safe location UPHILL and UPWIND.
2. **Brush off immediately** droplets visible on the skin with a blunt object, such as a credit card, stick, edge of a book or a tongue depressor. **Take care not to break or scratch the skin.**
3. **Blot up droplets** with absorbent material. Dirt, flour, soap detergent and other absorbent material will work.
4. **Remove clothing** after visible droplets are removed from the skin and continue cleaning your body with what is available (listed in order of preference)

    - Soap and water: first wash affected areas, then the entire body. Be careful of eyes, mouth, ears and other body openings.

    - Water: If soap is not available, flush with water.

    - Absorbent material: If water is not available, use dirt, flour or other materials over the affected areas. Be careful to avoid contact with eyes, mouth, ears and other body openings.

5. Put on clean clothing if available. Medical responders should supply gowns.

6. If other victims are scared, talk to them and try to calm them. Let them know if help is on the way.

Taking action if emergency services don't arrive

If emergency services do not arrive after you leave the immediate danger area or within 15 minutes, use the evacuation procedures to go the nearest hospital for an examination. If your are in a sealed room and have not heard from emergency services, plan for your evacuation upon reaching one hour of the safe time limit of air supply.

If emergency services do not arrive after you leave the immediate danger area or within 15 minutes, use the evacuation procedures to go to the nearest hospital for an examination.

Nuclear events

A nuclear explosion is also a large-scale radiological emergency — creating much more radioactive material than even the largest radiological devices. Even if you are not in the area affected by the blast and fires, you may need to evacuate. This is especially true if you are downwind of the explosion. In such cases, it may be necessary to evacuate even if you are at a distance of tens or hundreds of miles.

A nuclear explosion or attack is highly unlikely to occur.
Source: FEMA News Photo.
2003/0564521

Nuclear protection

Take the following actions seconds after a nuclear explosion to protect yourself. Know that the shockwave will pass over you twice and then debris will begin to fall.

1. Do not look at the light from the explosion.
2. Move out of the line of sight of the explosion.
3. Take immediate cover:
   - **Indoors:** move below a desk, table, bed or other cover away from windows or other glass objects. Basements and lower-level floors are better than upper-level floors.
   - **Outdoors:** Move as low to the ground as possible. Go into a ditch, behind an embankment, hill, wall or thick structure. Keep all barriers between yourself and the explosion.
   - DO NOT JUMP IN WATER. The water will be hotter than the air and will stay hotter longer.
4. Cover exposed skin.
5. Cross your legs to be as stable as possible.
6. Open your mouth and cover your ears with your hands to prevent ruptured eardrums.
7. Stay under cover until debris stops falling.

What do I do after the blast?

Due to the size of a nuclear explosion, it is important to consider that emergency responders will probably not be able to handle the entire incident. Therefore it is not likely that help will come from fire, police, EMS, National Guard or others for days or weeks. More than likely, you will have to take action after a nuclear explosion.

When do I evacuate?

The most important decision you make immediately following a nuclear explosion is deciding whether to stay and seek shelter or depart from the blast area. Either action could save your life. **If fires are widespread and appear to be growing they could form into a massive blaze called a firestorm (see next page). You MUST evacuate. Do not enter a fallout shelter.**

Evacuation procedures

You may have to walk one to 15 miles or more before you come into contact with people who can help you. Victim assistance sites would most likely be set up along major roads leading out of the affected areas.

1. Move away from the blast area.
2. Cover as much of your body as possible.
3. Cover your mouth with a wet rag.
4. Move away from the center of the blast area.
5. Move UPWIND.
6. Do not take anything from the blast area.
7. Consider all objects, especially metal objects (jewelry, keys, and so on) to be contaminated with radiation.
8. Avoid patches of loose soil or dust; if forced to walk through these, do not disturb.

Once you are out of the area damaged by the blast

1. Seek medical help.
2. Change clothes.
3. Remove all articles of jewelry or any other items.
4. Shower.
5. Find transportation further from the site and out of the fallout zone.
6. Contact family members.

Dangers after a nuclear explosion

Firestorm

Firestorms form when many fires turn into a single, massive fire igniting even the air. A firestorm may take several hours to build-up but once it starts it will spread quickly carried by super-heated winds, which may burn for days. Fallout shelters will not offer protection from a fire storm because of the extreme heat. It tends to use the all of the available air that you need to breathe.

Fallout

Fallout is the raining of radioactive particles out of the cloud of debris tossed up by a nuclear explosion. Fallout generally begins about 20 minutes after the nuclear explosion and continues for many days or even weeks. Most fallout will occur directly beneath the blast site and downwind as the cloud of radioactive debris drifts away.

NOTE: You will only have the option of using a fallout shelter if the fires appear to be small and are not widespread.

Fallout is the raining of radioactive particles out of the cloud of debris tossed up by a nuclear explosion. Fallout generally begins about 20 minutes after the nuclear explosion and continues for many days or even weeks.

Fallout shelters

Opinions vary regarding the usefulness of fallout shelters. Some believe that a fallout shelter is the best place to seek shelter following a nuclear blast. Others think that the danger of fire or building collapse is too great and it is better to evacuate the area of blast and fire as soon as possible. Consider your options and risks to decide what is best for you — given the rare chance a nuclear explosion could occur.

If you choose to use fallout shelters, know that some cities provide fallout shelters for citizens to use. If shelters are not provided, you may consider preparing your own. A fallout shelter should have the following characteristics:

- Underground
- Sealed from outside air
- Few doors and windows (all doors and windows can be closed)
- Emergency 'go-kit' supplies for at least 2 weeks

Avoid using using water from sinks, baths or anything else connected to pipes because the ground water may be contaminated and dangerous.

Entering a fallout shelter after an explosion

If possible keep abreast of news broadcasts via radio or contact outside sources via cell phone. You may have to stay in the fallout shelter for days or weeks before outside radiation reaches safe levels.

Leaving a fallout shelter

Exit a fall out shelter if authorities announce it is safe to evacuate, two weeks have passed or food and water run out. Do everything you can to minimize your contact with a contaminated environment. When leaving a fallout shelter, follow the evacuation procedures listed on page 158.

Opinions vary regarding the usefulness of fallout shelters.

Quiz yourself, family and friends

1. How can you find out what the hazardous materials sources and dangers are in your community?

2. How is a company spilling or releasing hazardous materials similar to governments or terrorists using Weapons of Mass Destruction on civilians?

3. Thus far, what has been the impact of terrorist groups using chemical, biological, radiological or nuclear materials to harm civilians?

4. What are the seven self-protection responses?

5. What is brush and blot?

Find out the answers to the Chapter 9 quiz on page 202.

Part 4
Recovery

Expect food shortages after an emergency. The Martinez family needed the help of the Salvation Army to re-stock food after Tropical Storm Allison in Houston, TX. Source: photo by Andrea Booher, FEMA. 2003/0564524

After an Emergency: What Do I Do Now?

"The next step is sometimes the hardest," says Adam Rowe, a landscaper from the small town of Rough and Ready in the Sierra foothills, about the recovery of the California wildfires. "The emergencies are over and you've got to find out how bad things are."

"Act now to remove ash and protect soil,"
by Douglas Kent, *Los Angeles Times,* November 6, 2003

Introduction

Emergencies can strike quickly and, without warning, can possibly disrupt your life. They can force you to evacuate your neighborhood or confine you to your home. In addition, disasters have the potential to cut off basic services, such as electricity, telephone, gas, and water. The interruption of these services, combined with forced evacuation or confinement, make dealing with and sometimes surviving the aftermath of a disaster difficult and frustrating.

If you make use of the tools emergency management authorities provide as well as your planning outlined the chapters of *Part 2: Preparation,* you and your family will be better equipped to deal with the short- and long-term effects of a major disaster. Furthermore, with thorough planning you may not need emergency assistance, freeing response resources for those in dire need. In this way, your own preparedness is an asset to the community.

Note that emergency services may become overwhelmed following a major disaster. In general, the larger a disaster, the longer it will take for emergency services to reach all those affected. Your family's supplies, know-how and resources are likely the only assistance you will have immediately following a disaster. The emergency services recommend that you prepare to be self sufficient for at least the **first 72 hours following a disaster.**

Chapter Overview

This chapter provides tips on restoring normalcy after an emergency:

- The first few days
- Government assistance
- Long-term effects of a disaster
- Media interview requests
- Volunteer opportunities

Listen closely for news updates on a battery powered radio after an emergency.
2003/0564523

Make sure children have games and activities to do while recovering from an emergency.
2003/0564526

Going through the first few days

If a disaster occurs in your community, it is important first to ensure the safety of yourself and your loved ones. Provide whatever aid you can to others only after you have recovered. Below are a few basic considerations to help you through the first few days following an emergency:

1. Remain calm.
2. Sustain life. If necessary give first aid or CPR if people are hurt.
3. If you have a functional phone or other form of communication, notify the out-of-town family contact person and appropriate agencies of your home status, such as, utilities companies.
4. Make requests for emergency assistance — if needed.
5. Comfort those who are in distress. Let them know that help will arrive in due course.
6. Listen to the advice of local emergency response officials. If you have a radio or if the television is working, turn to news stations for important updates and instructions.
7. Conserve your resources. Food, water, medicine and other supplies you have stocked may need to last for many days.
8. Entertain your children as much as possible with the resources available.

Shelter-in-place

If you must shelter-in-place, remain inside your home, place of work or where ever you can find protection for an extended period of time if necessary. If possible, find a battery-powered radio to keep abreast of any updates.

When sheltering-in-place, make sure that you shut your doors and windows securely. In some cases, such as during a hazardous material spill, you may need to go to a top story room, shut the windows and turn off the ventilation system. See *Chapter 9: Hazardous Materials and Weapons of Mass Destruction* for more information about sheltering-in-place during a hazardous material release.

Power outage

If you experience a loss of power, expect that utility companies may not be able to assist immediately. If you have a generator, it is very important to run it outdoors where poisonous fumes can ventilate into open air. **Do not run an electric generator indoors.** A number of people have died of carbon monoxide poisoning resulting from the incorrect use of household generators.

Water

Make sure that you stock an ample supply of water and food. Water is critical for the human body and makes up to 60 percent of an adult's weight and up to 80 percent of an infant's weight. A person can live several days without food but only a few days without water. The Federal Emergency Management Agency (FEMA) cautions against rationing water because of its great importance. Drink at least 2 quarts per day, as long as supplies last and/or look for other sources.

Water sources

If you are unable to drink tap water because of cut off services or contamination, consider using other sources inside or outside of your home. FEMA suggests the following alternatives as well as water purification procedures to use when tap water is unavailable.

In the home

- Melt ice cubes
- Toilet tank: the water in the tank (not the bowl) is safe to drink only if chemical treatments have **not** been added.
- Hot water tank
    - Turn off the power that heats it and let the tank cool.
    - Place a container underneath and open the drain valve at the bottom of the tank. Do not turn the tank on again until water services are restored.
- Water pipes: release air pressure into the plumbing system by turning on the highest faucet in the house. Then drain the water from the lowest faucet.

Outside the home

These sources can provide water but may **require purification**:

- Rain water
- Spring water and water from streams
- River, lakes
- Coiled garden hoses

Water purification

Pay attention to local news and radio for boiling orders or other drinking water safety instructions. Sterilize tap water that is cloudy or designated as unfit for drinking as well as water from outside sources, such as rainwater. Non-sterilized water may be contaminated with the parasite *Giardia*. To sterilize water, you can boil it or use bleach when boiling is not an option.

Water is critical for the human body and makes up to 60 percent of an adult's weight and up to 80 percent of an infant's weight. A person can live several days without food but only a few days without water.

To sterilize water, you can boil it or use bleach when boiling is not an option.

*Houston, Texas June 19, 2001—
These children are at the
Salvation Army Distribution
center in Houston, Texas that
provided disaster relief
essentials. Source: photo by
Andrea Booher, FEMA.
2003/0564524*

Boiling

Boiling water is the preferred method of purification because disease-causing microorganisms cannot survive the intense heat.

- Strain water containing sediment or floating material through a cloth or paper filter.
- Bring water to a rolling boil for 1 minute.
- Pour the water back and forth from one clean container and add a pinch of salt to another to improve the taste.

Bleach

Plain household chlorine bleach may be used if hypochlorite is the only active ingredient. Do not use bleach with soap or fragrance.

- Strain water containing sediment or floating material through a cloth or paper filter.
- With an eye dropper, add 8 drops of bleach per gallon of water (16 if the water is cloudy), stir and let stand.
- After 30 minutes, the water should taste and smell of chlorine. At this time it can be used.
- If the taste and smell (and appearance in the case of cloudy water) has not changed, add another dose and let stand. **If after one half hour the water does not have a chlorine smell, do not use it.**

Food

Keep non-perishable food items, such as canned goods, in your food stockpile. It is best to use food that requires no preparation or cooking. High calorie, protein and vitamin non-perishable foods are ideal. If the water supply is low, eat low salt foods, such as unsalted nuts, cereals and crackers. Many canned, non-perishable food are high in sodium that will increase your thirst. Take multivitamins to help maintain your body's vital nutrients. In the event of large scale disasters, look for announcements of temporary food distribution centers to re-stock your food supply.

Damage assessment

If a utility is turned off, wait for a professional from the utility company to turn it back on. Do not do it yourself.

If you are returning from a mandatory evacuation order, upon returning look for any damage in your home. If you find damaged or broken electrical wires, gas or water lines, shut off the utility. If a utility is turned off, wait for a professional from the utility company to turn it back on. Do not do it yourself.

Check for fires, fire hazards and for chemical spills

- Starting at the water heater and then moving throughout your home, smell for gas leaks.
- If you detect the smell of gas or suspect a leak, have everyone leave the home quickly, turn off the main gas valve and open windows.
- Do not light matches, candles or turn on electrical switches until you have inspected your home for gas leaks.

In some cases, a civil engineer employed by the state may have already inspected your home. If your home was determined to be structurally unsound, you will not be able to live there until the problem is corrected or repaired. In these cases it is important to contact your insurance company and FEMA to find out if shelter and monetary aid are available for you and your family.

For guidance on safely assessing specific disaster damage, see *Chapter 8: Natural Disasters and Accidents* and *Chapter 9: Hazardous Materials and Weapons of Mass Destruction.*

Secondary emergencies

Sometimes, large-scale disasters set off secondary emergencies. Food supplies may be low in the community making restocking food and water difficult. Looting of stores and vandalism may occur which would also limit access to restocked supplies. Therefore it is important to restock disaster supplies as soon as you and your family are safe.

Assistance

Government response

Overall, the larger the scope and impact of the disaster, the longer it will take for the government to provide assistance. If your community is declared by the President to be a Major Disaster Area, FEMA will set up a toll free number to handle requests for federal disaster assistance.

FEMA disaster recovery assistance

FEMA coordinates a wide range of federal disaster assistance across federal agencies to help people and communities recover.

- Grants for temporary housing, home repairs and replacement of essential household items
- Grants to replace personal property and to assist in meet medical, dental, funeral and transportation needs

Jackson, TN, May 28, 2003 — FEMA Employee Earl Yamashita helps a customer at the Mobile Disaster Recovery Center set up on East Chester Street in Jackson, Tennessee.
Source: photo by Mark Wolfe, FEMA News Photo.
2003/0564525

Moore, OK, May 17, 2003 — Michael Lampton and Marsilla Sadongei of the Small Business Administration inspect tornado damage. Source: photo by Bob McMillan, FEMA News Photo.
2003/0564504

Hurricane Isabel

With the flooding that followed after of Hurricane Isabel hit land, FEMA set up Disaster Recovery Centers in local neighborhoods to help individuals file for federal assistance. FEMA also helped local government representatives begin the claims process for funding repair damage to community roads, buildings and other infrastructure.

- Unemployment benefits for workers with disaster-related job losses
- Low-interest loans for uninsured residential, business and farm property losses
- Crisis counseling services: income tax assistance for casualty losses, advisory aid for legal needs, veteran benefits and social security matters

FEMA also assists community recovery efforts by providing funds to state and local governments for debris removal, emergency protective measures, the restoration of damaged infrastructure and measures that reduce future disaster risks.

Help outside of government agencies

As sad as it may seem, misfortune can bring out predators who seek to use the uncertainty and confusion that follow disasters to make a quick profit.

You should be wary of individuals or groups who offer to help and are not officially working for local, state or federal authorities or a reputable care-giving organization like the American Red Cross or the Salvation Army. As sad as it may seem, misfortune can bring out predators who seek to use the uncertainty and confusion that follow disasters to make a quick profit. If you're in doubt about whether an offer of help is legitimate, ask your local government representatives. The last thing you need at this point is to become a victim twice. Many times local governments will set up fraud hotline numbers following a disaster. If you become a victim of price gouging or the solicitations of an unlicensed vendor, these hotline numbers will provide you with the means to report any cases of wrongdoing and file complaints.

Hiring contractors

Try not to rush into starting repair work. Obtain estimates from more than one licensed and bonded contractor.

FEMA has outlined useful tips to help you find honest and affordable contractors to repair your home after a disaster. In cases where government aid is available, the agency may require an assessment of the damaged property before making any repairs. Try not to rush into starting repair work. Be very cautious about contractors you hire to repair damaged property. Obtain estimates from more than one licensed and bonded contractor. Ask your neighbors what they are paying for similar work and call the local Better Business Bureau to check out a contractor. Be wary of contractors claiming they can offer services 'fast and cheap.'

Proper licenses and insurance

- Write down the license plate number and driver's license number of someone offering services.
- Ask to see proof of the contractor's licenses and building permits.
- Make certain the contractor shows you a certificate of insurance covering liability and workers' compensation — otherwise, you could be sued if a worker is injured while working on your property.

Documents and contracts

- Be careful that your signature on a contractor's bid is not an authorization to begin work.
- Make sure both parties sign a contract stating: the job, start date, quality of materials as well as the cost and payment schedules.
- Have the contractor sign 'a release of lien' when the work is done and paid. This will prevent the contractor from making legal claims against your property in the event of a dispute later.
- Make sure repairs are done according to local building codes. For example, ensure all work that requires city or county inspection is officially approved in writing before making final payment to the contractor. If there is a large amount of damage, you may even want a structural engineer to double-check repairs before you make a final payment.

Payment

- If the contractor insists on payment for materials up front, then go with the contractor to buy them or pay the supplier yourself.
- Don't pay more than 20 percent down for the contractor to begin work. Pay as the work progresses.
- Don't make final payment until the job is finished and you are satisfied.
- Don't sign over an insurance settlement check to the contractor.

Contractor fraud

If you have been a victim of contractor fraud, contact your State Attorney General's Office of Consumer Protection and your local police department. To report fraud, waste, and abuse within a FEMA program call 1-800-323-8603.

Longer-term effects of a disaster

Unexpected changes in daily routines can cause added stress to you and your family in more than one area. For example, although you may not have been injured by an earthquake or tornado, the disaster may have destroyed your vehicle. Your home may have suffered extensive damage, requiring you to move to one or more temporary residences. Your children may be required to attend another school, leaving their friends and familiar teachers. Survivors of large-scale disasters should be aware of the effects of cumulative stress. Being able to 'choose your battles' and decide which tasks are important are part of the art of survival.

Negotiating with a Contractor

Make sure you cover all the bases before you hire a contractor.

- Proper licenses and insurance
- Clear documentation and contracts
- Agreed payment schedule before and after completed work

If you have been a victim of contractor fraud, contact your State Attorney General's Office of Consumer Protection and your local police department. To report fraud, waste, and abuse within a FEMA program call 1-800-323-8603.

Disaster damage can be very costly. Look at your finances and insurance to go over your options. 2003/0564527

Disaster Relief Help

Victims, including laid-off workers and small businesses, affected by natural disasters or national emergencies can receive free budget counseling from HOPE Coalition America.

Call 1-888-388-HOPE or visit www.hopecoalitionamerica.org.

Family

Disasters can also put a strain on families. A single stress factor may be manageable but many stresses combined may seem unbearable. This could involve having to uproot your family, apply for disaster assistance and recover from physical or emotional trauma that prevents you from taking care of your children or elderly parents. Recovering from a disaster is a lot of work and often parents may not be physically available to support children immediately. Sometimes parents may give extra responsibilities to children, such as watching other siblings or taking care of the household. Often, conflicts with spouses and other family members intensify so much that spousal and child abuse significantly increases in communities following a major crisis. You may also be forced to leave your home, permanently or temporarily. In these instances, living with relatives or close friends could also add to tensions. See *Chapter 11: Psychological Effects of an Emergency* for strategies on reducing stress and helping children recover and return to their normal routines.

Finances

Your finances may be shaken if you suffered damage during a disaster. Seeking financial assistance to rebuild and repair damage adds to the already high levels of disaster-related stress. The hassles of dealing with bureaucracy can further add to the frustration.

Assistance may come from insurance policies, government disaster funds or other traditional means. When calling your insurance company, make sure you have all of your policy information with you. If you protected your essential paperwork — stored it in your 'go-kit,' a safety deposit box and/or other fireproof container — it will likely be available for your use following a disaster. See section *Assistance* on page 167 for guidance on applying for federal disaster relief funds.

The non-profit disaster relief organization HOPE Coalition America provides free financial counseling for individuals and small businesses recovering from natural disasters and national emergencies. The volunteer counselors are senior executives and professionals from financial services, legal industries and other institutional organizations. HOPE Coalition America recently created a partnership with FEMA to coordinate their disaster relief services.

Work

Increased conflicts with colleagues sometimes accompany a disaster. Such conflicts are often the result of the added stress a disaster can bring into your life. Your work performance may suffer because of an inability to concentrate or fatigue. Often, companies must lay off employees following a disaster to recover their financial losses. This may directly affect you and also increase family distress.

Funerals

If you experience the tragedy of losing a loved one in your family or in your community, you may need to help arrange their wake and funeral while trying to bring your life back to normal. You can find funeral resources and options in the local newspaper, on the Internet or in bulletins from faith-based organizations or charity groups. After going through the painful steps of a organizing or attending a memorial service and making insurance claims, other documentation will require your time and concentration to ensure your financial and home-life stability. Refer to your home emergency 'go-kit' for important documents to settle your loved one's affairs. See *Chapter 11: Psychological Effects of a Emergency* for help in going through the grief process.

Difficult and painful processes, such as making arrangements for a funeral or life insurance claims, may be necessary for personal recovery.
2003/0564528

Talking to the media

If a crisis occurs, ordinary citizens can suddenly see reporters with bright camera lights in front of them broadcasting their comments across the country and even abroad. If you experience an emergency, especially if you play a role in responding to it, you may be asked to give an interview or even represent your community or organization at a press conference.

Should you accept the interview request?

First consider whether or not it is appropriate for you to do an interview. You are under no obligation to speak with media representatives if you do not feel comfortable. If you are suffering from emotional trauma, it may not be the best for you or the audience. If the interview is related to your duties at work or as a volunteer, make sure that you have permission to talk with the press. If you are an eyewitness in an ongoing investigation, check with law enforcement before making any statement to the media. Some information may not be appropriate for the public especially if there is an investigation or if families or others affected have not yet been notified.

Ask questions before committing to do an interview. Ask why you are being interviewed and what angle the report will take. Also, ask the reporter's name, media affiliation and station address and numbers. This will help you decide if you want to speak to this reporter/producer.

Children should not be interviewed because they could be going through psychological trauma and/or feel guilty about any mistakes they feel they made in the interview.

Media Interviews

Gary Tuchman, National Correspondent for CNN explains, "interviewing people going through a tragedy or crisis is not pleasant for me as a reporter. I have found, however, talking to a reporter is often cathartic for those who are grieving. When I have covered tragedies, I will ask someone if they want to talk with me and if they don't, I won't bother them again. If they want to talk, I tell them what I believe to be the truth: sometimes telling a story about their loved one on television in an accurate and compassionate way helps bring comfort to a family.

I take pride in promising a family that we will do a dignified story about their son who died in the World Trade Center or their daughter who died on the USS *Cole* and then report a story that touches viewers' hearts. I know when the viewers react that way, we've kept our promise to the bereaved family."

Plymouth, NC, September 21, 2003 — Volunteers help load water onto a truck that will deliver the boxes to local distribution centers. Hurricane Isabel knocked out all of the local utilities and residents were relying on food and water shipped into town. Source: photo By Dennis Wheeler, FEMA News Photo. 2003/0564530

Listen to the Experts

"Many times after disasters, volunteers can be more of a burden than a help, especially if the response agency does not have the capacity to accept offers," explains Louie Fernandez, Senior Bureau Chief of Miami-Dade Fire Rescue and Office of Emergency Management Public Affairs. "After Hurricane Andrew in 1992, volunteers showed up by the thousands, but there was no coordination, check-in or process to receive the help. A good point to remember: always wait for the disaster response representatives to ask for specific help before responding with your kindness."

Approach

If you decide to give an interview, the following are some helpful hints to keep in mind when dealing with the media. Some of these recommendations may seem for official spokespersons but everyday citizens can also be bombarded with media attention.

- First and foremost, be honest. Speak slowly and calmly.
- Talk only about what you know and what you saw.
- Keep in mind that you are speaking to an audience of people through a reporter — not just to the reporter.
- If you are on television, look at the interviewer while talking, not to the camera.
- Assume the microphone is always on and that anything you say could be quoted.

Don't be afraid to ask a reporter to rephrase a question, if needed. If a reporter asks a question indicating something that is untrue, clear up the situation without repeating the false statement. If you speak to many reporters, share the same information to make sure the story is consistent. Do not make any comments that you do not want to see in print or have aired on television or radio.

Volunteering and charitable donations

After a major crisis, make sure you are taken care of before committing your personal time to others. If you are interested in volunteering or making donations to support the victims, listen for specific requests from the government agencies responding to the incident before going to the site or their offices. If you join a volunteer campaign that supports a disaster that is outside of your community, plan on what transportation and items you might bring if you are needed for couple of days. See page 29 for potential organizations for which you can volunteer to help after an incident.

Quiz yourself, family and friends

1. How long should you be prepared to take care of yourself and your family after a disaster occurs?

2. What four main steps should you keep in mind in recovering from a disaster in the short-term?

3. If you have to turn off the utilities either before evacuating or upon finding a damaged utility, who should turn your utilities back on?

4. If a disaster doesn't affect your physical health, what other other areas of your life could it impact?

5. If a member of the media asks you to do an interview, what should you consider before accepting it?

Find out the answers to the Chapter 10 quiz on page 202.

An emergency can cause a range of psychological responses for adults and children that may take months or years to resolve.
2003/0564533

Part Five **Chapter 11**

Psychological Effects of Emergencies

Before September 11, 2001, four New Jersey women's lives revolved around family and children. When their husbands were killed that day, their view of the world changed.

Patty Casazza explains, "I had faith in all of my leaders on September 10th that they were doing the best jobs that they could to protect the lives of my loved ones, my friends, my countrymen."

Mindy Kleinberg said, "Whenever there's a tragedy, you think, 'How could this have happened?'"

Lori van Auken admits, "I thought democracy just worked. And I learned that it doesn't go like that. That if you want to live in this great country of ours, with our . . . different rights . . . and all the things that we take for granted, you have to fight for those things."

Kristen Breitweiser reveals, "I've turned into a very disenchanted, fully awake, no longer naïve person, who's extremely driven."

NOW with Bill Moyers, *PBS*, September 12, 2003

Introduction

Your ability to cope with the immediate impact of a crisis may determine your mental well-being in the days, months and even years ahead. A traumatic experience can cause shock and possibly emotional problems. Because people respond differently to traumatic events, you may react more strongly than others or you may hardly react at all. For this reason, be aware of your emotional state. If you begin to experience overwhelming feelings, ask for help from those close to you and, if necessary, mental health professionals.

Chapter Overview

This chapter provides explanations and guidance on addressing the emotional responses people experience after trauma including:

- Five stages of crisis recovery
- Handling stress
- Common traumatic stress reactions
- Five stages of grief
- Child trauma recovery

Banding together

The *Four New Jersey Women* banded together after their husbands died in the World Trade Center attack on September 11, 2001. When they heard the Bush Administration and some Congressional members were trying to block a broader investigation of the attack cause, the widows decided to organize a protest in Washington, DC. The widows wanted to go beyond the probe limited to the FBI and CIA to find out what the airlines, the immigration service and White House knew and did before and on the morning of 9-11. They started by making signs at the hardware store which indeed led to the White House.

After their protest attracted hundreds of citizens, members of Congress and the media, the White House invited the widows and a few other survivors for a series of meetings — some reportedly angry. President Bush changed his position and Congress agreed to launch a new, independent commission to investigate how 9-11 happened and how the Bush administration will prevent future attack attempts. Tim Roemer, commission member and former congressman, says the commission wouldn't exist if it weren't for the research and inspiration of the *Four New Jersey Women*. One widow, Kristen Breitweiser, gave Roemer her husband's wedding ring explaining, "A couple months after 9–11 they found that ring that's in your hand. That's all I have left of my husband . . . and I want to be able to tell [my three year–old daughter] someday what happened to her father and what happened to the country." Breitweiser insists, "we must, as a country, grow and be made stronger and safer by the bitter lessons learned on September 11."

Source: *NOW with Bill Moyers*, PBS, September 12, 2003

Five phases of crisis recovery

The five phases of crisis recovery can help explain the natural process that occurs after a disaster on individual and community levels. First, the initial impact causes **shock and disbelief**, particularly to intentional acts of violence. Even if an expected natural disaster occurs, expansive damage, such as with Hurricane Andrew, can still cause shock and overwhelming feelings.

Second, the **heroic** period starts in response to need with first responders and citizen's going beyond the calls of duty to save lives, volunteer as well as give donations and public praise.

Third, the **honeymoon** period begins with people forgetting or forgiving past hurts. New relationships and alliances can also occur. People may also support significant change that they otherwise would not consider before the crisis, such as new legislation.

Fourth, **disillusionment** sets in when those most severely affected experience the real and possibly long-term problems associated with the disaster. People may group into 'factions' and former disputes may re-occur. This fourth phase is also characterized by depression.

Lastly, **reconstruction** takes place, ideally with strong leadership, to restore normalcy and improve the situation. Reconstruction is hopefully done with medium and long term constructive actions based on the new options and agreement that the honeymoon period creates.

These phases are also consistent with the stages of grief explained on pages 183-185. Understanding both can allow you to embrace, not fight, this inevitable change regardless of how little or great the impact of the emergency. In doing so, you can recover and help others grapple with these physical, spiritual, emotional and psychological challenges.

Handling stress

Stress is the pressure we experience mentally and physically in response to both positive and negative events in our lives. It is a reality that we deal with everyday. Negative stress is associated with problems and challenges, such as a big deadline, job loss or car trouble. Positive stress is associated with new, exciting opportunities, such as starting a new job, traveling to a foreign country or buying a home. Both can impact your health and how you manage your daily life. Adults may react to stress in many ways that can include the following:

- Increasing substance use and/or abuse
- Paying less attention to family and work responsibilities
- Feeling depressed and anxious

To handle stress and cope with a crisis, first understand stress and normal reactions to a traumatic event. People cope with stress in different ways. Some people cry and some laugh whereas others may become angry. Some people renew or embrace their religious beliefs. Both adults and children react to stress but have different recovery needs.

What is traumatic stress?

Traumatic stress includes the thinking process as well as physical, emotional and behavioral reactions people often experience after an upsetting event. These reactions serve as a personal defense mechanism. If you don't allow yourself to process the traumatic event by sharing it with others close to you, shedding these painful feelings will be more difficult and take more time. For example, guilt, shame and intense anger may interfere with recovery. For many, substance use or abuse is the first reaction to everyday stress and, in turn, to coping with a crisis as well. Consuming substances will make it more difficult for you to go through the inevitable aftermath of trauma because you would be masking your feelings as well as adding toxins to your body. No reaction is necessarily 'wrong' as long as your reaction does not cause harm to yourself or others. Your reactions should eventually lessen ideally to the point of disappearing.

Positive results can also emerge from a traumatic event particularly during the heroic and honeymoon periods of crisis recovery. Positive career changes, renewed appreciation of family and friends and/or increased volunteerism are some examples of positive changes people make after tragedies.

Factors affecting traumatic stress

Before taking action on negative or positive effects of a crisis, make sure you identify your feelings and how you feel most comfortable in recovering. The following factors affect a person's reaction to traumatic stress:

- Severity of the trauma
- Duration of the disaster
- Number of times the person has previously experienced trauma
- Negative reactions and/or level of support from family and friends

To recover as quickly as possible from an incident, make your best effort to avoid using and abusing substances.
2003/0564532

If you don't allow yourself to process the traumatic event by sharing it with others close to you, shedding the pain will be more difficult and take more time.

Traumatic stress reactions

The following chart lists the cognitive (thinking), physical, behavioral and emotional symptoms you may have after an incident.

Reactions	Symptoms	
Cognitive	Confusion Poor problem-solving Difficulty calculating Heightened anxiety Memory impairment	Distractibility Inattention Disorientation Lowered alertness Poor judgment
Physical	Rapid heart rate Tremors Intestinal upset Nausea Sleep disturbance Elevated blood pressure	Chills Dizziness Chest Pains Headaches Fatigue
Behavioral	Difficulty sleeping Startle response Appetite change Isolation Fatigue	Nightmares Hyper–vigilance Withdrawal Avoidance Substance abuse
Emotional	Guilt Fear Shock Sadness Irritability	Anger Anxiety Disbelief Hopelessness Numbness
Grief process	Shock/denial Anger Acceptance	Bargaining Depression

Traumatic stress disorders

The symptoms of traumatic stress are normal reactions to an abnormal event that can manifest in related disorders such as the following.

Fear and anxiety

Fear and anxiety are common and natural responses to a traumatic situation. For many, fear and anxiety may linger long after the trauma has ended.

Fear and anxiety are common and natural responses to a traumatic situation. For many, fear and anxiety may linger long after the trauma has ended. This happens when a person's view of the world and sense of safety have changed. Triggers or cues that can cause anxiety may include places, times of day, certain smells or noises or any situations that remind you of the trauma. As you begin to pay more attention to the times you feel afraid, you can discover the triggers for your anxiety. In this way, you may learn that some seemingly out–of–the–blue anxiety is really triggered by something or some place that reminds you of your trauma.

Traumatic reminders

People who have been traumatized often re-experience the traumatic event. For example, you may have unwanted thoughts of the trauma and find yourself unable to stop thinking about them. Some people have flashbacks, or very vivid images, as if the trauma is recurring. Nightmares are also common. These symptoms appear because a traumatic experience is so shocking and so different from your everyday experiences that you can't fit it into what you know about the world. Seek professional help if you have been in multiple traumatic events. In these cases, signs of stress may not surface for months.

Increased reflexes

Beyond responding to immediate danger, other common responses to trauma include increased reflexes and arousal, such as feeling jumpy, jittery, or shaky, and/or having trouble concentrating or sleeping. Continuous arousal can drain you of energy and lead to impatience and irritability, especially if you're not sleeping enough or on a regular schedule.

Arousal reactions come from what is known as the 'fight or flight' response in your body. When we protect ourselves from danger by either fighting or running away, we need much more energy than usual. To do so, our bodies pump out extra adrenaline to give us the extra energy we need to survive.

People who have been traumatized often see the world as filled with danger. Some people place themselves on constant alert always ready to respond immediately or 'fight' any attack. Increased arousal is useful in truly dangerous situations, such as in facing an attacker. However, constant alertness misdirects and decreases your energy particularly when it continues for a long time and even in safe situations. (This is why it is important to take the time to understand the risks in and near your community to be alert efficiently, not excessively.) Another reaction to danger is to freeze, like a deer caught in headlights, and this reaction can also occur during a trauma. Extreme responses to fear — hyper-vigilance or complete inaction — can stop you from conducting your life normally.

Avoidance

Avoidance is a common way of managing trauma-related pain. Most commonly, people avoid situations and/or thoughts that remind them of the event. Often they avoid places, such as the place where it happened, or they avoid situations that are somewhat related to the trauma, such as going out in the evening if the trauma occurred at night.

Traumatic Stress Disorders

These disorders are a normal reaction to abnormal events.

- Fear and anxiety
- Traumatic reminders
- Increased reflexes
- Avoidance
- Anger and irritability
- Guilt and shame
- Changed self-image and/or view of the world
- Grief and depression
- Difficult sexual relations
- Substance use and abuse

Having extreme responses to fear — hyper-vigilance or complete inaction — can stop you from conducting your life normally.

Most commonly, people avoid situations and/or thoughts that remind them of the event.

Sometimes the painful thoughts or feelings may be so intense that your mind just blocks them out altogether and you may not remember parts of the trauma.

Another way someone might try to reduce discomfort is by pushing away painful thoughts and feelings. This can lead to feelings of numbness when you find it difficult to have both fearful and pleasant feelings. Sometimes the painful thoughts or feelings may be so intense that your mind just blocks them out altogether and you may not remember parts of the trauma. However, sometimes the avoidance begins to extend far beyond reminders of the original trauma to all sorts of situations in everyday life. This can become so severe that people can become virtually housebound or only able to go out with another person.

Anger and irritability

Anger and irritability can also accompany trauma. People may feel angry over how the event could have been avoided by their or others' actions. Anger can also occur out of a lack of control throughout the experience. When people constantly feel irritable, they may express it in the form of anger. It may be especially confusing to feel angry with those who are closest and most supportive of you. If you are caring for someone experiencing trauma, try not to take their anger personally to the extent you are not harmed or taken advantage.

Guilt and shame

Trauma often leads to feelings of guilt and shame. Many people blame themselves for things they did or didn't do related to the event.

Trauma often leads to feelings of guilt and shame. Many people blame themselves for things they did or didn't do related to the event. For example, some assault survivors believe that they should have fought off an assailant and blame themselves for the attack. Others feel that if they had not fought back they wouldn't have gotten hurt. Sometimes, other people may blame those around them for the trauma. It is important to understand that feeling guilty about the trauma means that you are taking responsibility for what occurred. Although this may make you feel somewhat more in control, it can also lead to feelings of helplessness and depression.

Self-image and views of the world

Self-image and views of the world often become more negative after a trauma.

Self-image and views of the world often become more negative after a trauma. Many people see themselves as generally more negative after the trauma and tell themselves such thoughts as, " I deserve this because I am a bad person." They also tend to feel that they can't trust anyone. Relationships with others can become tense and it may be difficult to become intimate with people as your trust decreases.

For people who used to think the world was a safe place, the trauma may suddenly make them think that the world is very dangerous. Sometimes people develop a distrust of the government and begin to question whether or not the government can protect them. If you have had previous bad experiences, feelings of trauma convinces you that the world is dangerous and others aren't to be trusted. These negative thoughts often overwhelm people and make them feel as if the trauma has changed them completely. These feelings can decrease feelings of self–determination or control. Trauma can change your view of the world but it doesn't have to change who you are or your abilities.

Trauma can change your view of the world but it doesn't have to change who you are or your abilities.

Grief and depression

Because trauma can greatly change how you see yourself and the world, it makes sense to feel sad and to grieve for what you lost because of the trauma. The depression can include feeling down, sad, hopeless or despairing. You may cry more frequently. Trauma may cause you to lose interest in people and activities you used to enjoy. You may also feel that plans you had for the future don't seem to matter anymore or that life isn't worth living. These feelings can lead to thoughts of wishing you were dead or doing something to hurt or kill yourself.

You may also feel that plans you had for the future don't seem to matter anymore or that life isn't worth living. These feelings can lead to thoughts of wishing you were dead or doing something to hurt or kill yourself.

Sexual relationships

After a traumatic experience, many people find it difficult to feel sexual or to have sexual relationships. This is especially true for those who have been sexually assaulted. In addition to the lack of trust, sex itself is a reminder of the assault. If people engage in sexual relations too soon, they may feel more vulnerable. In these cases, taking things step by step will allow you to gauge how ready you are to return to having intimate sexual relations.

Substance use and abuse

Some people increase their use of alcohol or other substances after a trauma. There is nothing wrong with responsible drinking unless your use of alcohol or drugs changed as a result of your traumatic experience. It is not a constructive way to deal with these feelings because it provides only temporary relief and causes a host of additional emotional, psychological and physical problems. For example, substance use or abuse can slow your recovery, add toxins to your already stressed body and possibly cause or worsen dependency.

Substance use or abuse can slow your recovery, add toxins to your already stressed body and possibly cause or worsen dependency.

Can trauma reactions happen at the same time?

Often the reactions to trauma are connected to one another. For example, a flashback may make you feel out of control and will therefore produce fear and arousal. Many people think that their normal reactions to the trauma mean that they are 'going crazy' or 'losing it.' These thoughts can make them even more fearful. If you stay aware of the changes you have gone through since the trauma, as you process these experiences during treatment the symptoms should become less distressing and eventually subside.

Often the reactions to trauma are connected to one another.

Try to avoid substance use or abuse to mask your pain from a traumatic experience.
2003/0564534

Can feelings of trauma cause negative reactions?

Some emotional responses could lead to actions that make the situation worse for you and even the first responders managing the recovery. The following chart outlines these responses and their possible consequences.

Thoughts	Reactions
Vicarious Rehearsal	Visualize own involvement Consider effect of response on them Reject response plan and offer another Falsely feel at risk and desire attention
Denial	Ignore warnings Find the warning confusing Refuse to believe threat or effect
Stigmatization	Community refuses services or access Community diminishes risks to a group
Fear/Avoidance	Act personally to avoid a threat Irrational and danger to others
Withdrawal/ Hopelessness/ Helplessness	Feel powerless Lack effort for precautionary action May ignore messages to evacuate

Source: CDC Crisis and Emergency Risk Communications, September 2002

Post-traumatic Stress Disorder (PTSD)

Post-traumatic Stress Disorder (PTSD) causes people to have intense fear and strong physical reaction long after the danger has passed. Traumatic stress reactions usually subside within two months after the event. Strong reactions are common and understandable but they are serious and can affect the way you live your daily life. If symptoms last beyond two months, seek professional help. Being aware of the changes you've undergone since the trauma is the first step toward recovery.

The majority of traumatized individuals do not develop PTSD. The number of people diagnosed with PTSD varies from about 4 to 30 percent of those who are in traumatic incidents. The majority of adults, especially men, adjust quickly after a disaster or an act of mass violence. Children and mothers with young children are the most likely to suffer PTSD feelings of helplessness and fear also for a longer period of time. Regardless of the group, if any person experiences the following symptoms for longer than two months, they should seek professional help. See section *Caring for Children* on page 186 on noticing if your children are suffering from emotional trauma and how to speak with them about these issues.

Symptoms of PTSD

Re-experiencing the traumatic event

- Recurring nightmares
- Intrusive daydreams or flashbacks
- Dis-associative experiences
- Traumatic reminders

Avoidance or numbing

- Avoiding thoughts, feelings, activities, or situations that are associated with the trauma
- Feelings of detachment or alienation
- Inability to have loving feelings

Increased arousal

- Exaggerated, startled response
- Insomnia and other sleep disturbances
- Irritability or outbursts of anger
- Physiological reactions to reminders, such as anniversaries or court dates

Mothers and their young children are the most likely to suffer from feelings of fear and helplessness after an emergency. 2003/0564533

Going through the grieving process

People have their own methods for dealing with the loss of a loved one. As people grieve, they should be encouraged to use natural sources of support and to talk with friends, family and co-workers — at their own pace. They should follow their natural inclinations about how much and with whom they talk.

Grief has been characterized as having five stages: denial, anger, bargaining, depression and acceptance. The following is a brief description of the stages; however, people may go through them in a different order and/or more than one at a time.

Denial

During the denial stage, it is common for people to refuse to believe what has happened. Sometimes shock and disbelief accompany denial. In severe cases, people can retreat to an altered mental state by re-enacting rituals that occurred before the loved one died. For example, someone might make an extra cup of tea for the loved one who is no longer there or flashback to times and conversations in the past as though the loved one is there now. The denial stage can last for several days.

Five Stages of Grief

Everyone has different ways to deal with grief but it is important to reach out to others to express your feelings. Follow you own natural inclinations about how much and with whom to talk. Grief has been characterized as having five stages:

- Denial
- Anger
- Bargaining
- Depression
- Acceptance

If you or your loved one is having suicidal thoughts following a death of a loved one or a traumatic event, consult a professional immediately to seek help.

'Death out of time' of a young person, such as a parent's child, can be especially difficult to mourn. 2003/0564536

Anger

The anger stage can manifest itself in many ways. Blame is a common way that individuals deal with anger. Sometimes they blame others for their loss. Irritability may also accompany anger and people may easily have emotional outbursts. People often become angry with themselves. Extreme anger can interfere with recovery and relations with others at home, at work and in the community. People must be careful not to turn this anger inward either by hurting themselves or not sharing their feelings with family, friends or a grief counselor.

Bargaining

Often the person who grieves offers something to change the reality of what has happened. For example, a person may want to bargain with a deity or themselves to bring back the loved one. If a loved one is near death, such as nearing the end of a fatal disease or in a coma, the person will also bargain to restore the their loved one back to health.

Depression

Depression is very likely to happen for people grieving. Most people in this stage indicate feeling listless and tired and others may say they feel like they are being punished. Many people no longer feel pleasure and joy from activities that previously delighted them. They may also develop unjustified feelings of guilt and self–blame and feel that the experience was their fault, even when this is clearly not true. For example, a victim of an industrial disaster may feel guilty for not having noticed an impossible-to-hear noise in the engine that came before a fatal explosion.

Sometimes the depression can become so severe that people feel that life is no longer worth living. If you or your loved one is having suicidal thoughts following a death of a loved one or a traumatic event, consult a professional immediately to seek help.

Substance use and abuse

People experiencing depression, clinical and/or event-related, may also turn to alcohol or drugs to try to numb their pain. This is especially likely for people who have battled with addiction. Many times people restart former addictions, such as consuming drugs, alcohol or nicotine. This may also cause guilt for 'falling off the wagon' adding to the challenge of recovery. They may also misuse prescription or over-the-counter medication. Although this may seem to be an understandable reaction, substance abuse worsens the person's symptoms and makes the situation much more difficult to improve. Alcohol and drugs can provide only temporary relief and make a bad situation worse in the long run. Facing the problem without alcohol or drugs will help you recover sooner and with fewer problems.

Restarting old bad habits is common after emergencies. Resist the urge to restart smoking under crisis-induced stress. 2003/0564535

Acceptance

The final stage of grief is often confused with recovery. Sometimes a person can accept the loss and never recover. Acceptance occurs when the grieving person realizes that life has to go on. People who arrive at this stage are typically able to regain their energy and can establish goals for the future.

Traumatic grief

When the loss of a loved one is sudden, disturbing and/or violent, people may not follow the 'normal' grief process. When they think of the lost loved one, they may experience intrusive images of how that person died and have many disturbing thoughts about what the loved one experienced before death. Reminiscing about the loved one may not ultimately lead to positive memories. In this instance, it is important to seek professional help to manage your feelings and the bereavement process as much as possible.

Healing strategies

How can I help myself and others recover?

The following strategies will help you when dealing with your own or a loved one's traumatic stress reactions:

- **Protect**: help ensure the safety, privacy, health and self-esteem of yourself and others.
- **Connect**: help people communicate support with family, peers and mental health service providers. Listen actively and supportively but do not probe for details and emotional responses. Let the person say what they feel comfortable saying without pushing for more.
- **Detect**: look for symptoms in yourself and in others who have severe traumatic stress reactions.
- **Direct**: organize, prioritize and plan your life and help others with the next steps of recovery.
- **Select**: go to and recommend that others seek physical, spiritual, and mental health as well as social and financial services as needed.
- **Validate**: use educational materials from trusted sources on television, radio, Internet as well as handouts from doctors' and government offices to affirm the normalcy and value of your and others' reactions. This also includes any concerns, ways of coping and goals for the future.

Depression is a natural stage of grief. Allow yourself to experience the five stages of grief to mourn your loved one. 2003/0564537

Life's Chapters

"We hear the word 'closure' used repeatedly after a tragic event," says Gary Tuchman, National Correspondent for CNN who has covered news for over 20 years. "We hear well-meaning people ask grieving relatives to try to bring about 'closure.' Well, 'closure' is a word that should be banished when it comes to discussing tragedies. People don't ever 'get over' horrific tragedies. They go through phases: from disbelief to despair to anger to depression to loneliness and more. The order is different for each person. The magnitude of the feelings varies but people do not just 'get over it.'

Instead of the cliche 'closure,' think about those different stages as experiencing 'chapters' as time passes. A true friend understands 'getting over it' doesn't happen in the real world. What we all need to do is keep in mind that someone who suffers the loss of loved one will go through these different chapters for years to come."

Seek out ways to care for yourself physically to recover from psychological trauma. 2003/0564538

Personal interaction

Some additional tips to putting the general health strategies into action include spending time with others, thinking about the event and putting yourself in a calming environment.

- Spend time with people you know well and like.
- Talk about the event and don't try to block recollections.
- Avoid thinking about the event only in terms of yourself or taking on responsibility for how others are responding.
- If you have to make a tough decision or one with great consequences, ask for help to think things over.
- Participate in a peer discussion group if you have the opportunity to do so.
- Seek out comfortable and familiar surroundings.
    - Avoid stressful stimuli and media, such as videos and movies that may remind you of the event.
    - Avoid volunteering for high stress jobs at work when personal stress is high.

Physical habits

Your eating, exercise and sleeping habits affect your health on a regular basis and it is especially important to take special care of yourself when recovering from trauma.

- Eat fresh vegetables with higher protein levels, fruit, whole grain breads and pasta; avoid high sugar foods.
- Drink up to 64 ounces of water per day.
- Avoid stimulants, such as caffeine, chocolate and nicotine.
- Avoid depressants, such as alcohol and other substances.
- Rest when you feel tired.
- Exercise according to your doctor's advice.

Caring for children

How can disasters and crises affect children?

Emergencies can often cause a range of quick reactions or even reflexes among children and adults. A traumatic incident that children witness or are involved in can temporarily or even permanently hurt their physical and emotional health. If a fellow student or an adult from the community commits a violent act, the children may lose their trust in other children and/or adults throughout their lives. Since society tries to instill trust in adult authority figures and in peers as friends, intentional acts of violence or even emergencies can cause children to experience confusion and fear.

Recovery may take months and years depending on who was involved, what type of event occurred and how soon the child received help — similar to adults. Whether a child is caught in an emergency or learns about it, parents and caretakers need to know what child trauma symptoms are and how to help children understand their feelings. If a child shows post-traumatic disorder symptoms after six to eight weeks, seek help from a mental health professional. The following information is derived from a section of *Jane's School Safety Handbook* written by Marlene Wong, Director Crisis Counselling and Intervention Services at Los Angeles Unified School District and Director, School Crisis and Intervention Unit at the National Center for Child Traumatic Stress, UCLA and Duke University.

How can I help a child recover from a traumatic event?

Giving a traumatized child immediate attention will start the healing process and prevent further pain. Understanding what can traumatize children and how to listen and talk to them are simple, yet very important things to know and do. Because children and styles of raising children are not the same, the following sections provide options for parents/caretakers to consider.

- What could traumatize children?
- What should I ask a child who suffered from an accident?
- What should I tell children dealing with a loss of a loved one?

What could traumatize children?

Minor accidents can scare and affect them, such as a child falling off a bike accident, but in most cases they can easily recover. Major accidents that are life-threatening or that are caused by people, nature or mechanical breakdowns can affect a child more seriously. Although every emergency is different, children may suffer the consequences in similar ways. The more extreme examples could include a child who desperately escapes from a collapsing or an exploding building. A child who hears unanswered cries for help or who has a long and difficult separation from parents/caretakers, siblings and other close relatives can also be affected. A sudden, unexpected death of a family member, close friends or neighbors could also impact a child's health. Witnessing a high degree of violence for a short or long time can cause child trauma.

What should I ask a child who suffered from an accident?

Children who witness and/or experience traumatic events need direct and constant supervision to help them understand and deal with their feelings. Close attention to these children can help the healing process and prevent them from experiencing more pain and even life-long problems. If children directly witnessed or experienced the emergency, consider asking the following questions to understand what happened to them and their

Children can experience the same reactions as adults after an emergency. 2003/0562498

Impact of 9-11 on New York City Kids

The May 2002 report "Effects of the World Trace Center Attack on NYC Public School Students," for the New York City Board of Education estimated that over 26 percent of students in New York City Schools experienced some form of post-traumatic stress disorder, anxiety disorders (including fear of public places) and depression six months after the September 11 attacks. The findings also included increased alcohol use and abuse among high school seniors. The report researchers including: Applied Research and Consulting, Columbia University Mailman School of Public Health and New York State Psychiatric Institute are currently looking into the longer-term impact.

Although every emergency is different, children may suffer the consequences in similar ways.

Make sure children do not see news coverage of violent acts as it can have long-term impact on their physical and emotional health. 2003/0564539

reaction to the event. Dr. Robert Pynoos, Director of Trauma Psychiatry at UCLA, developed these questions to follow initial triage treatment.

- How were you feeling that day right before the event happened?
- What was the scariest moment?
- Do you feel afraid of anything? How much?
- Have you had any bad dreams? What were they and when did you have them? Could you go back to sleep after the dream?
- What kinds of things remind you of what happened, such as sights, sounds or smells?
- Is there anything that you see, hear or smell that makes you think it will happen again?

Pay close attention to the small details of their stories. As with adults, elements may occur in daily life that could trigger scary memories or an emotional episode. For example, a familiar smell, color or sound could trigger a painful memory for the child and prevent them from doing something as routine as tying their shoes or taking a bath.

Helping a child go through the grieving process

Dealing with the tragedy of losing a loved one, perhaps in the event that an emergency, can make a child have even more complex and fearful emotions. Having them tell you what they are thinking and feeling is critical for them to heal and for you to be aware of their well-being. Share their grief and the healing process. Make sure that you tell the child it is OK to feel bad and that they are not alone. Let them know how you feel and let them help you feel better and do so in kind.

Explain there is a grieving process that includes similar feelings for both children and adults. A child may first experience disbelief that may turn into anger. This reaction helps them distance themselves from the loss. Even with little or no hope for a recovery, they may tell themselves that they can do something to solve the problem. Feelings of regret or responsibility from past incidents (no matter how small or big) may allow children to believe the situation can improve. Sooner or later, sadness and crying occurs as the child begins to understand that life needs to continue without the person. Depending on the child, he or she may feel forgiveness and a sense of peace about what happened for the first time. The child may still feel sad but has stopped trying to fight reality.

Consider these options when talking to a child who has lost a loved one.

- Ask if they have thoughts or dreams about the person/people who died.
- Ask if they are worried about who will take care of them if something like this happens again.

- Explain they could also experience physical effects of their loss, such as fatigue or difficulty sleeping, loss of appetite and/or trouble focusing.
- With the child, find an enduring way to pay tribute to the life of the person who has died.

These next sections are broken up across age groups of preschool and early elementary (ages 3 to 7), older elementary and middle school students (ages 7 to 13) and adolescents (ages 13 to 18).

- What are symptoms of child trauma?
- How do I discuss issues of safety, feelings and behavior changes?
- How should I care for a child after an emergency?

Preschool and early elementary age children

Symptoms of child trauma (ages 3 to 7 years)

Very young children have few coping skills to deal with psychological trauma and violence. Keep a close eye on these symptoms and consider the suggested options as it fits each child's personality.

Actions

- Feeling helpless
- Experiencing paralyzing and generalized fear
- Acting confused
- Unable to talk about fears and concerns
- Engaging in traumatic play, as in reenacting the incident repeatedly

Change in habits

- Showing regressive symptoms, such as thumb-sucking, bed-wetting and baby talk
- Experiencing sleeping problems including nightmares
- Having eating problems, including loss of appetite or refusal to eat

View of the world

- Showing separation anxiety, such as clinging behavior and fear of being alone, difficulty being away from parents or worrying about when parents will return

Discussing safety, feelings and behavior changes

Using your regular behavior, tell children that you care for them and that they are safe. If you appear panicked, the children will feel upset as well. Give concrete examples of what is being done for their safety, especially

Media Coverage Impact on Kids

Media coverage can have a long-term physical and emotional impact on children and adults. The media's tone, repeated messages and choice of imagery may also increase or cause negative emotional responses for the general viewing audience. With this in mind, view television with care and seek additional media sources, such as radio and print.

Two years after the Oklahoma City bombing, 16 percent of children and adolescents who lived approximately 100 miles from Oklahoma City reported significant post-traumatic stress disorder (PTSD) symptoms related to the event. PTSD occurs when the physical and emotional responses to a traumatic event continue to affect people after the danger has passed. This is an important finding because these youths were not directly exposed to the trauma and were not related to victims who had been killed or injured.

PTSD symptoms were greater in those with more media exposure and in those with indirect interpersonal exposure, such as having a friend who knew someone who was killed or injured. Therefore, always be careful of what television programs your children watch.

Source: B. Pfefferbaum et al. 'Posttraumatic Stress among Children after the Death of a Friend or Acquaintance in a Terrorist Bombing,' *Psychiatric Services*, 51, 2000, 386–388.

Children need to keep their regular schedules, such as a routine dinner time, in addition to eating healthy foods while recovering from trauma. 2003/0564540

when they express fears. They need to know that people are doing everything possible to solve the problem. Although you should make your best effort to remain calm, tell children that their feelings of fear, anger and sadness are normal emotions. Many adults and children feel that way after acts of violence or emergencies. Helping children of this age identify these feelings may be the first time they do so or to this magnitude. If children do not share these feelings, encourage them to tell you their thoughts and feelings when they feel afraid in the future.

Caring for a small child after an emergency

A peaceful, safe environment is critical for all children, particularly after an emergency that may have threatened their personal safety. Consider these steps to calm them and start the healing process:

- Make sure they have quiet time and a familiar place to rest.
- Set up a calm routine with the same caretakers.
- Maintain as regular daily routine as possible.
- Feed them healthy, comfort food, such as starches (whole grain breads, pasta, oatmeal, grits, potatoes, rice) and fresh fruit and vegetables. Avoid foods and beverages with sugar and caffeine.
- Turn off televisions and remove traumatic reminders of violence and disorder.

Older elementary and middle school students

Older children attempt to understand emergencies, particularly violent acts, through the ideas of responsibility, fairness and assumption of guilt. Some can engage in heated discussions of right and wrong, blame and just punishment.

Symptoms of child trauma (ages 7 to 13 years)

Generalized and irrational fears can overwhelm older elementary and middle school-aged children's ability to cope, similar to very young children. They may act out or experience the following:

Actions

- Facing traumatic reminders of the violent act that cause additional fears
- Telling and retelling details of the traumatic event
- Reenacting the incident or playing games that include some type of trauma
- Being afraid of being overwhelmed by their feelings
- Acting in hostile, aggressive and/or bullying ways toward friends, neighbors and classmates

Habit changes

- Having trouble eating with an upset stomach or little appetite
- Having trouble sleeping and/or having night scares, such as a fear of ghosts
- Being afraid of routine things: being alone, going to certain places, going to sleep
- Doing things they did when they were younger: thumb-sucking, sleeping with parents, clinging to teachers and parents

View of the world

- Worrying that something bad might happen to parent(s), caretaker(s), sister(s) and brother(s) and other close family and friends

Trouble in school

- Showing decreased concentration and poor coping skills in the classroom
- Refusing to leave the classroom during the day, not wanting to play in an open playground

You may want to also ask the child's teacher if the child has been more aggressive or withdrawn or reenacting the event or rescue scene.

Discussing safety, feelings and behavior changes

Using your regular behavior, tell them that you care for them and that they are safe. If you appear panicked, they will feel upset as well. Give concrete examples of what is being done for their safety, especially when they express fears. Discuss what they are thinking and feeling to help them understand their reactions. This may also help them identify physical symptoms when they feel afraid.

Children of this age group typically know what fear, anger, shame, sense of isolation and sadness feel like but are still learning what these emotions are and how to deal with them. As with smaller children, explain these are normal emotions that adults also feel after acts of violence or emergencies. They need to know that it is all right to express these feelings. This could include such questions as:

- What would help you feel safer?
- What makes you feel sad?
- What helps to make you feel better when you are feeling sad?
- Have you had any bad dreams and thoughts of revenge?

Organize fun activities for children, especially ones that include exercise. 2003/0564541

Take Action

It you feel a child is experiencing trauma based on your discussions, consider finding professionals available to help. This could include a teacher, counselor, social worker, psychologist or other school staff member designated to assist and support students after a crisis.

If you appear panicked, the children will feel upset as well. Give concrete examples of what is being done for their safety, especially when they express fears.

Give positive feedback about the way in which they were able to talk about difficult thoughts and feelings. Bring up specific behavioral changes the child has acted on and explain how those are common after a traumatic experience but are usually temporary. Also be sure to explain how impulsive and reckless actions are symptoms of stress.

Caring for older elementary and middle school children
Children from the approximate ages of 7 to 13 have some abilities to take care of themselves but they are still very sensitive to their surroundings. Consider these steps to create a calming and safe environment and avoid any future pain or trouble for the child.

- Monitor television programs and avoid traumatic reminders of violence.
- Make sure they have quiet time and a familiar place to rest.
- Feed them healthy, comfort food, such as starches (whole grain breads, pasta, oatmeal, grits, potatoes, rice) and fresh fruit and vegetables. Avoid foods and beverages with sugar and caffeine.
- Set up a calm routine with the same caretakers.
- Give clear limits and reinforcement of expected behavior at home and at school.
- Refuse to tolerate aggressive, hostile, risk-taking or bullying behavior toward others.
- Encourage the child to ask questions or communicate with adults when they have difficult moments during the school day.

Adolescents

Adolescents can exhibit a wide range of emotions in response to emergencies, particularly targeted violence. Discuss with your children behavioral changes and explain how those are common after a traumatic experience but are usually temporary. If you feel the adolescent is experiencing trauma based on these discussions, consider finding professionals available to help. This could be a teacher, counselor, social worker, psychologist or other school staff member designated to assist and support students after a crisis.

Symptoms of adolescent trauma (ages 13 to 18 years old)
Adolescent symptoms consist of complex feelings and behavior that can be considered child-like or adult-like because they are between those life stages. Because adolescents are more independent, some trauma signs may occur away from your view. Therefore, pay close attention to a variety of clear and subtle changes to see if your child suffers from trauma.

Feelings

- Detachment, denial and/or guilt
- Shame about their fear and vulnerability fearing their peers and youth culture would disapprove

Habit changes

- New or increased risk-taking or life-threatening behavior, such as drug or alcohol abuse, promiscuous sexual behavior, criminal or delinquent acts, traffic violations
- Regressive behavior, such as thumb-sucking, sleeping with parents, clinging to teachers and parents
- Abrupt changes in friendship or abandonment of friendships
- Adult behavior, such as becoming pregnant, leaving school, marrying

View of the world

- New fears or worries such as something bad might happen to parent(s), caretaker(s), sister(s) and brother(s) and/or other close family and friends

Trouble in school

- Decrease in attendance, performance and/or interest in their extra-curricular activities
- Engaging in fights

Discussing safety and feelings

Discuss a range of emotions and issues with adolescents from the emergency at hand to their feelings about society in general. First, tell them how much you care for them and at all times speak in a calm yet confident and controlled manner. Children follow the example of adults as role models. If you appear panicked, they will feel upset as well. Give concrete examples of what is being done for their safety, especially when they express fears. They need to know people are working to solve the problem. Discuss what they are thinking and feeling to help them understand their reactions. This may also help them identify physical symptoms when they feel afraid. Explain how you feel and how you are dealing with similar concerns to show it is all right for them to express these feelings. This could include asking:

- What would help you feel safer?
- What makes you feel sad?
- What helps to make you feel better when you are feeling sad?
- Have you had any bad dreams and thoughts of revenge?
- What can I do to help?

Horsham, PA June 20, 2001 — Youth volunteers at the Red Cross Service Center serve a hot meal to flood victims. Source: photo by Liz Roll, FEMA News Photo. 2003/0564542

Stress-relieving Activities for Kids

1. Provide activities or suggest resuming team and individual sports, dance, art, breathing exercises and working on a short-term project

2. Parents/caretakers should spend extra time to help with homework, chores, projects and activities.

3. Encourage participation in activities on behalf of the victims, the school and/or the community.

4. Encourage activities that promote a renewed sense of control and justice. They may work to reduce their sense of helplessness.

5. Ask what kinds of things teachers can do at school to help them feel safe. Is the class planning a project to help?

Praise them for their efforts.

Mirror back important aspects of their story to show you are listening and make sure they know what they are saying is true. Discuss specific behavioral changes in your adolescent and try to see and explain how such changes are common after a traumatic experience. Tell them that these responses are usually temporary. Throughout your conversations, give positive feedback about the way in which the child was able to talk about difficult thoughts and feelings.

Giving explanations

When you explain that many adults and children share these thoughts and feelings, you will help adolescents know that their responses are normal and in reaction to an extraordinary and difficult situation. Your household may be strained because of stress from the event.

Consider discussing the actual event and media coverage. Ask for your adolescent's opinions and ideas but be sure to correct misinformation and distorted fears. Give concrete examples of existing safety measures. Explain how impulsive and reckless behaviors are symptoms of stress on personal and societal levels.

Do adolescents need to be taken care of?

Although adolescents have different levels of independence in how they live their daily lives — with some driving cars, caring for younger siblings and relatives, and contributing to the household finances — it is important to make sure they have a calming, comfortable environment in which to recover and readjust. Recent research has shown that parental supervision remains important for adolescents who have more freedom but may not have the mature judgment to match their growing independence.

- Attempt to monitor television programs and help them avoid traumatic reminders of violence.
- Make sure they have a quiet time and a familiar place to rest.
- Return to or set up a calm routine with the same caretakers.
- Feed them healthy, comfort food, such as starches (whole grain breads, pasta, oatmeal, grits, potatoes, rice) and fresh fruit and vegetables. Avoid foods and beverages with sugar and caffeine.
- Give clear limits and reinforce expected behavior at home and at school.
- Watch closely for signs of substance use and abuse.
- Refuse to tolerate aggressive, hostile, risk-taking or bullying behavior toward others.

Consider discussing the actual event and media coverage. Ask for your adolescent's opinions and ideas but be sure to correct misinformation and distorted fears.

Although adolescents have different levels of independence in how they live their daily lives — with some driving cars, caring for younger siblings and relatives, and contributing to the household finances — it is important to make sure they have a calming, comfortable environment in which to recover and readjust.

Quiz yourself, family and friends

1. What are the five stages of crisis recovery?

2. What are the five stages of the grieving process?

3. What is Post-traumatic Stress Disorder?

4. Name five of the symptoms of child trauma.

5. When helping a child deal with the loss of a loved one, what is a critical response?

Find out the answers to the Chapter 11 quiz on page 202.

Part 5
Reference

Chapter 12. Appendices

CBRN characteristics

The following provides information on the history and background of chemical, biological, radiological and nuclear (CBRN) materials used as weapons of mass destruction (WMD).

Chemical weapons

People normally think of chemical attacks in terms of World War I: soldiers scrambling to put on gas masks to protect themselves from clouds of white or yellow gas floating across the battlefield. Chemical weapons have become much more diverse and sophisticated since the early 1900s but still need specific conditions, such as weather, to harm people.

Characteristics of chemical weapons

Depending on these conditions, chemicals that are highly volatile will disperse rapidly; whereas, more persistent chemicals can present a hazard to your skin and lungs for several days or more. In urban areas, those persistent chemicals can last longer since the buildings will absorb and then slowly release the chemicals over time.

- **Form**: solid, liquid or gas. Vapors and clouds may or may not be visible.
- **Odors**: some chemical materials associated with military use have a distinctive odor (such as, bitter almonds, freshly cut-hay, geraniums), but many other are odorless or so fast acting that the victim is incapacitated before they can react to the scent.
- **Effect**: a rapid and noticeable effect on unprotected people, animals and plants; some will discolor their surroundings.

Biological weapons

The nature of disease makes initial detection and recognition of such a biological attack far more difficult than in the case of an airborne chemical or biological release. Often the first signs of exposure to a biological agent are symptoms of illness. These symptoms can take days or even weeks to begin to appear. This means that signs of a biological attack don't become apparent until the exposed person is far from where contact with the infectious substance was made. Recognition of dangerous biological substances is, therefore, often a question of noticing and reporting a suspicious activity or item before symptoms appear.

Tokyo Subway Attack

The most notable terrorist use of a chemical weapon was the attack on the Tokyo subway by members of the Aum Shinrikyo cult in 1995. Bags of an odorless, colorless and deadly liquid nerve agent known as sarin were spilt open on the floor of subway cars during rush hour. Many people came into contact or inhaled the sarin but others were able to evacuate the trains before collapsing. Others continued to board the trains and were then exposed. In total, 8 people died almost immediately with 4 deaths within hours. Over 5,000 people were injured.

Anthrax Letters

In October 2001 anthrax attacks, off-white powders containing a disease were sent through the mailing system to a number of media and political figures. In all, 5 people were killed and 22 were injured in the attacks. The disruptive aspects of the attack were severe as well. White powder of any sort, including chalk dust and other harmless substances, became a cause for alarm. The mailings also precipitated numerous copycat hoaxes in which baby powder, talc or other powders were sent packed in letters bearing no return address. Paying attention to media reports and government guidance during such incidents is key to understanding the best way to protect yourself while staying calm.

Whatever the size or overall impact of the device used, radiological devices are more of a means of causing **mass disruption** (fear, panic, psychological trauma) than a true weapon of mass destruction.

Characteristics of biological weapons

- **Dried form**: powdery substance that could be amber, brown, yellow, pink, red or off-white in color. Dyes can be added to confuse recognition by color.
- **Texture**: very fine and can be disturbed by the slightest movement of air.
- **Liquid form**: liquid agents have similar colors as they are based on the substance from which the agent was developed.
- **Consistency**: slightly thicker than whole milk.
- **Effect**: symptoms are delayed.

Toxins

Another category of biological agents is toxins. Toxins are poisons rather than diseases and most have a more rapid onset than infectious diseases, such as anthrax or smallpox. For example, a person attacked with toxins, such as botulinum toxin and ricin, will experience symptoms after one to 12 hours.

Radiological weapons

Depending on the concentration and radioactive strength of the material, radiation damage would not occur immediately, if at all. If undetected and untreated, it could take days, months or years for some dirty bombs — bombs packed with radiological material — to generate casualties. This is particularly true in urban areas where building materials, such as concrete, would provide some shielding.

Characteristics of radiological weapons

Radiation alone is invisible, odorless and tasteless. The basic design of a radiological weapon or 'device' is based on packing radioactive material inside or around a bomb. The bomb is then exploded in order to spread radiological material as widely as possible. A range of radioactive materials could be used in radiological device:

- **Low-level** radioactive materials: those used in medicine and research as well as low grade, unenriched uranium.
- **High-level** radioactive materials: enriched uranium, plutonium and fuel rods from nuclear power plants. High-level materials are quite rare outside of the major nuclear powers although there is an illegal international market for such materials and there have been reports of missing materials in the former Soviet Union.
- **Color**: Most commercially available radiological materials appear metallic, such as cesium used in medical equipment and military or reactor grade substances, such as uranium and plutonium. They tend to glow in low light and are warm to the touch. They have a high density and a greater weight by volume than lead.

- **Effect:** if high level dose, immediate symptoms occur; if low level dose, symptoms are delayed.

Three main types of radiological weapons

1. **Radiological Dispersal Devices**, also known as 'dirty bombs,' use conventional explosives to spread or disperse radiological material.
2. **Simple Radiological Dispersal** is the deliberate spreading of radioactive material, for example, by adding radioactive material to food or water supplies to cause radiation poisoning or placing radioactive materials in an envelope and mailing it to a specific person.
3. **Simple Radiological Dispersal Devices** combine radioactive material with a non-explosive scattering device, such as a fan or atomizer.

Nuclear weapons

Countries like North Korea possess the ability to produce nuclear weapons and there is the possibility that such weapons may be unintentionally transferred from countries including Russia, China or Pakistan. That said, a remote but real possibility exists that such weapons may fall into the hands of individuals with the intent to use them.

Characteristics of a nuclear explosion

A nuclear explosion is the detonation of a bomb containing a critical mass of nuclear fuel. The effects of such an explosion would be many thousands of times that of bombs containing dynamite, plastic explosive, gasoline or other chemical mixtures. An easy way to put a nuclear explosion into context is that even the largest conventional bombs produce effects that rarely encompass more than one city block. A nuclear explosion would directly affect an entire city. Though highly unlikely, this kind of attack could result in disaster on a massive scale.

In addition to intense light, heat and a highly destructive series of shock waves, a final affect of a nuclear explosion is an electromagnetic pulse. This pulse could damage or destroy electronic equipment (cell phones, computers, televisions, radios, and anything with an electronic component) in direct line of sight of the explosion for many miles. This could not only knock out almost all ability to obtain information from the government on what to do after an attack, but could also severely hamper response efforts.

Radioactive Iodine

In 2000, a Japanese pharmaceutical worker was arrested after stealing a small bottle of radioactive Iodine-125 from the refrigerator at his lab and releasing it into a subway station in Osaka. The small amount of material represented a very low level of radioactivity and no one was injured.

Quiz answers

Chapter 1: Why Should I Use This Planning Guide?

1. D. Risks are proportional to your age, neighborhood and lifestyle.

2. Terrorists target organizations that represent cultural, human, government/military or economic value.

3. The "Eight-step Plan to Emergency Preparedness" is an outline to organize your disaster plan with your family and others involved in your life whether with your school, work and community.

    1. Find out what risks are in your area and government services available to help.
    2. Create an emergency response plan with your family and friends while keeping in mind needs of your school, work and community.
    3. Organize emergency supplies for home and on-the-go.
    4. Repair and ready your home for likely risks.
    5. Prepare personal affairs in the event you need to recover from an emergency.
    6. Understand how to protect yourself from risks in your area.
    7. Learn how emergencies impact your relationships and even your self-image and view of the world.
    8. Find out how you can offer your skills to help others in need before, during and after emergencies.

4. Before responding to an emergency, the three processes you should think of are:

    1. **Observe** the situation, taking in any unique or unusual circumstances.
    2. **Decide** on what the appropriate response should be, if any.
    3. **React** accordingly.

5. Your preparations can make you more independent of first responders allowing them to attend to others with greater needs.

Chapter 2: Government Protection: Who Does What and What to Expect

1. The role of law enforcement during emergencies is to be the first to arrive on the scene and ensure that it is safe for other first responders. Police apprehend/detain dangerous persons as necessary, cordon off areas that may be dangerous to the public, provide protection and support for victims and eyewitnesses.

2. Local agencies are the first to arrive and respond to an emergency. If they need additional help, they call the state for resources from their response agencies and the National Guard as well as volunteer organizations. Once these groups respond and assess the damage, the governor may make a Major Disaster Declaration and commit state funds for recovery and request for federal funds to help. The Federal Emergency Management Agency (FEMA) will review the governor's request and recommend action to the White House for the President to decide if the incident is a Presidential Major Disaster Declaration.

3. D: When a large number of people need emergency medical treatment and the local hospitals run out of beds, alternate care facilities will be set up in your community and announced through the media.

4. During an emergency, the media provides updated news and events, locations and hotlines for public services and guidance from authorities on self-protection measures.

5. Options for volunteering include the American Red Cross, Citizens Corps and its sub-sets (Medical Reserve Corps, Volunteers in Police Services (VIPS) and Community Emergency Response Teams (CERT)) and USA on Watch among other local and national private/non-for-profit charity groups.

Chapter 3: Personal Disaster Preparedness

1. When preparing for a disaster consider preparing your home, vehicle, school and work.

2. False. Not all safe rooms are for the same purpose or in the same location. They vary for tornados, hurricanes and floods as well as for hazardous materials releases.

3. C: You should evacuate when you receive an order from authorities or no safe shelter is nearby during an emergency.

4. D: Before seeking shelter, make sure it will provide you with more safety than evacuating.

5. The three types of documentation that you should organize and put in a fireproof area with copies in your go-kit should be government-issued, financial and personal documents.

Chapter 4: School Safety: Have You Done Your Homework?

1. When talking to children about school safety, discuss how to communicate with family members, travel safely to and from school and protect themselves while home alone.

2. To help children avoid bullying, encourage them to join school activities involving sports, art or other interests and help them develop another relationship with a supportive adult at school.

3. Yes, parents and guardians can see a summary of a safe school plan. The full plan can be very long and some information is non-releasable. Overall, schools must have tested and updated plans for any emergency that could happen on school grounds or during school-sponsored events.

4. If the school evacuates, be prepared to pick up your child at an announced location away from the school and show your identification to school officials. Make plans with the school ahead of time if there is a chance a relative or caregiver will be picking up the child.

5. Yes, day care centers, elementary schools, middle schools, high schools and universities must have different emergency plans because of the different age and abilities of the students. Specific language and disability programs must also have special procedures in place.

Chapter 5: Security in the Workplace

1. Your employer should put measures in place to limit your exposure to the following risk factors that attract robberies, which is the leading cause of high workplace homicide: working with the public, with cash, alone, at night, in high-crime areas and/or at or near high-profile targets.

2. The key areas where you can protect yourself from harm at work involve access controls, enclosed or isolated areas, leaving work, working late, bomb threats and suspicious letters, items or packages.

3. If someone calls and threatens to detonate a bomb at or near your workplace, note the following: exact time of call, everything the caller says, caller characteristics (age and gender) and voice description (mood, accent, clarity, familiarity, disguised).

4. Before going to your employer, seek out local social services and non-profit domestic violence organizations to help you because different levels of protection exist. They can inform you on how to best protect yourself and your job.

5. OSHA recommends that organizations establish a violence prevention program, perform a comprehensive work site analysis; eliminate/minimize identified hazards and provide comprehensive training and education to employees with qualified trainers.

Chapter 6: Street Smarts and Travel Safety

1. If you feel uncomfortable, threatened or think someone is following you, leave the area. Go to a well-lit, public area, such as a shop, restaurant or hotel, which often have security guards. Act confidently and as if you know where you are going, even if you don't.

2. Consider the following precautions when using an ATM:
   - Use ATMs during the day.
   - Be aware of your surroundings.
   - Go to an ATM with friend when possible.
   - Guard your personal information number (PIN) from public view.
   - Secure your cash in your bag or wallet before leaving the machine.
   - Beware of distractions pickpockets can use.

3. If someone follows you by foot or car, stay away from him or her. Don't respond to their questions or offers and don't go near the person or car. Go to a crowded, well-lit place where others can help.

4. When traveling to other countries, you must follow their laws.

5. Before leaving for your trip make sure you have the following information and/or documents: emergency contact information, photocopy of your passport and driver's license and an extra set of photos, insurance coverage, airline ticket and telephone numbers, and credit card and traveler's check numbers.

Chapter 7: Staying Alert and Reporting Incidents

1. If you see something out of the ordinary, keep a minimum distance of 300 feet — one football field or a city block. Do not put yourself in harms way to collect information.

2. Odd elements involving a vehicle could include: suspicious activity, location or action, occupants and/or changes to vehicle appearance.

3. This person could be there for the wrong reasons. Consider whether he has a valid reason for being at that location, such as the owner is re-starting the project or selling the site. Is this person's vehicle properly identified as from government or business? Note his appearance and actions: hair (gray, curly about shoulder length), height (about 6 feet tall), age (between 35-45 years), clothes (white shirt, blue jeans, wearing a white hard hat with a tool belt), and actions (using a ladder).

4. Depending on the child, as soon as she/he is of the age to understand the concept of strangers, explain they should never allow strangers into their home or accept any offer from someone they do not trust, such as a car ride, packages, candy, money or any other item.

5. When reporting an incident, remain calm and speak in a clear, easy-to-understand tone. Do not speak too fast. You may need to repeat the report. Remember to move to a minimum distance of 300 feet before using cellular communications to make a report.

6. **CHALET** is a general method for reporting incidents and stands for: **C**asualties, **H**azards, **A**ccess routes, **L**ocation, **E**mergency services available and **T**ype of incident.

Chapter 8: Natural Disasters and Accidents

1. D: A **Hurricane Watch** is issued when hurricane conditions — rain, winds in excess of 75 mph and tides 25 feet above normal (storm surge) — are possible within **48 hours**.

2. E: The best place to take shelter in the event of a tornado is in a basement or storm cellar.

3. C: If the authorities issue a mandatory evacuation order in the event of a flood, immediately leave for higher ground.

4. B: When confronted with a wildfire, move away from the blaze at right angles.

5. C: During a hurricane, most people die from the storm surge, or large waves, along the coastline.

Chapter 9: Hazardous Materials and Weapons of Mass Destruction

1. Many communities have Local Emergency Planning Committees (LEPC) that identify industrial hazardous materials and inform the public of potential risks. Companies that have hazardous materials are supposed to provide annual reports to LEPC.

2. Whether either party causes a small or large incident, the impact, illegal nature and ways to protect yourself are the same.

3. When terrorist groups have used chemical, biological or radiological elements, it has thus far resulted in mass *disruption* of the areas targeted rather than mass *destruction* of people and places.

4. Seven self-protection responses can be quickly referenced to help you protect yourself if a chemical, biological or radiological release is known or suspected. Recognized signs and symptoms are:

    1. **Remain calm:** beware of panic **created** from your own or other's fears.
    2. **Cover mouth, nose and skin:** block exposure with available protection (wet scarf, mask). If a contact hazard is suspected, cover exposed skin.
    3. **Move away from the source of the agent release to a safe area:** decide to either a) evacuate the building or area UPWIND and UPHILL, b) shelter-in-place above ground or c) seek shelter nearby.
    4. **Stay away from the general population:** contact with other persons may place them at risk of contamination.
    5. **Contact emergency response personnel** (police, fire, medical, National Guard): once you are safely away from the contaminated areas, wait for emergency responders for 15 minutes then continue to evacuate.
    6. **Beware of delayed effects:** some chemical and most biological and radiological agents take effect over a long period of time.
    7. **Help others:** Calm other victims who are scared.

5. The *brush and blot* method can be used to remove liquid chemical droplets from your skin.

    1. **Brush** off immediately droplets visible on the skin with a blunt object, such as a credit card, stick, edge of a book, tongue depressor. **Take care not to break or scratch the skin.**
    2. **Blot** up droplets with absorbent material. Dirt, flour, soap detergent and other absorbent material will work.

Chapter 10: After an Emergency: What Do I Do Now?

1. Understand that emergency services might be overwhelmed and may not be able to get to your location immediately. Emergency services recommend that you be prepared to be self sufficient for the **first 72 hours after a disaster**.

2. Immediately after an emergency, remember four main courses of action:

    1. Remain calm.
    2. Be patient.
    3. Sustain life. If necessary give first aid or CPR to people who are hurt.
    4. Listen to the advice of local emergency response officials. If you have a radio or if the television is working, tune into the news stations for important updates and instructions.

3. Never turn utilities back on yourself, wait for a company representative to do so.

4. Unexpected changes in daily routines represent additional stress that could impact your finances, work, home or school.

5. First consider whether or not it is appropriate for you to do a media interview. If you are suffering from emotional trauma, it may not be best for you or viewers as you may say something misleading or inaccurate when under duress. If the interview relates to your work or volunteer duties, make sure you have permission to talk with the press.

Chapter 11: Pyschological Effects of Emergencies

1. After a disaster, five stages generally tend to occur on personal and community levels to help restore normalcy and put preventive measures in place.

    1. Shock and disbelief
    2. Heroic period
    3. Honeymoon period
    4. Disillusionment
    5. Reconstruction

2. Post traumatic Stress Disorder (PTSD) are feelings of intense fear and strong physical reactions that last four to six weeks after the danger of an emergency has passed.

3. Psychological recovery from an emergency can sometimes take months or even years.

4. Symptoms of child trauma include: feeling helpless, paralyzed and generalized fears, confusion, inability to talk about fears and concerns, engaging in traumatic play, showing separation anxiety, showing regressive symptoms such as thumb sucking, bed-wetting, baby talk, experiencing sleeping problems including nightmares and/or having problems eating.

5. Have children undergoing the grieving process tell you what they are thinking and feeling so that you can understand their symptoms and recovery needs.

Emergency Contact Phone Numbers

Family/Household Members

1. _____ day: _____ night: _____
2. _____ day: _____ night: _____
3. _____ day: _____ night: _____
4. _____ day: _____ night: _____

Police/Fire/EMS: 9-1 -1 _____

Doctor: _____ Hospital: _____

Insurance policy #: _____ Poison Control: _____

Emergency Contact Phone Numbers

Family/Household Members

1. _____ day: _____ night: _____
2. _____ day: _____ night: _____
3. _____ day: _____ night: _____
4. _____ day: _____ night: _____

Police/Fire/EMS: 9-1 -1 _____

Doctor: _____ Hospital: _____

Insurance policy #: _____ Poison Control: _____

Emergency Contact Phone Numbers

Family/Household Members

1. _____ day: _____ night: _____
2. _____ day: _____ night: _____
3. _____ day: _____ night: _____
4. _____ day: _____ night: _____

Police/Fire/EMS: 9-1 -1 _____

Doctor: _____ Hospital: _____

Insurance policy #: _____ Poison Control: _____

Emergency Contact Phone Numbers

Family/Household Members

1. _____ day: _____ night: _____
2. _____ day: _____ night: _____
3. _____ day: _____ night: _____
4. _____ day: _____ night: _____

Police/Fire/EMS: 9-1 -1 _____

Doctor: _____ Hospital: _____

Insurance policy #: _____ Poison Control: _____

Emergency Contact Phone Numbers

Family/Household Members

1. _____ day: _____ night: _____
2. _____ day: _____ night: _____
3. _____ day: _____ night: _____
4. _____ day: _____ night: _____

Police/Fire/EMS: 9-1 -1 _____

Doctor: _____ Hospital: _____

Insurance policy #: _____ Poison Control: _____

Emergency Contact Phone Numbers

Family/Household Members

1. _____ day: _____ night: _____
2. _____ day: _____ night: _____
3. _____ day: _____ night: _____
4. _____ day: _____ night: _____

Police/Fire/EMS: 9-1 -1 _____

Doctor: _____ Hospital: _____

Insurance policy #: _____ Poison Control: _____

Family Disaster Plan

Neighborhood Meeting Place:_____
(outside your home)

Evacuation Meeting Place:_____
(outside your neighborhood)

- Address:_____
- Phone:_____ Transportation:_____

Family Contact:_____

Phone: day:_____ night:_____

Source: Your Family Disaster Plan, Federal Emergency Management Agency and American Red Cross

Family Disaster Plan

Neighborhood Meeting Place:_____
(outside your home)

Evacuation Meeting Place:_____
(outside your neighborhood)

- Address:_____
- Phone:_____ Transportation:_____

Family Contact:_____

Phone: day:_____ night:_____

Source: Your Family Disaster Plan, Federal Emergency Management Agency and American Red Cross

Family Disaster Plan

Neighborhood Meeting Place:_____
(outside your home)

Evacuation Meeting Place:_____
(outside your neighborhood)

- Address:_____
- Phone:_____ Transportation:_____

Family Contact:_____

Phone: day:_____ night:_____

Source: Your Family Disaster Plan, Federal Emergency Management Agency and American Red Cross

Family Disaster Plan

Neighborhood Meeting Place:_____
(outside your home)

Evacuation Meeting Place:_____
(outside your neighborhood)

- Address:_____
- Phone:_____ Transportation:_____

Family Contact:_____

Phone: day:_____ night:_____

Source: Your Family Disaster Plan, Federal Emergency Management Agency and American Red Cross

Family Disaster Plan

Neighborhood Meeting Place:_____
(outside your home)

Evacuation Meeting Place:_____
(outside your neighborhood)

- Address:_____
- Phone:_____ Transportation:_____

Family Contact:_____

Phone: day:_____ night:_____

Source: Your Family Disaster Plan, Federal Emergency Management Agency and American Red Cross

Family Disaster Plan

Neighborhood Meeting Place:_____
(outside your home)

Evacuation Meeting Place:_____
(outside your neighborhood)

- Address:_____
- Phone:_____ Transportation:_____

Family Contact:_____

Phone: day:_____ night:_____

Source: Your Family Disaster Plan, Federal Emergency Management Agency and American Red Cross

Emergency 'go-kit'

Organize the following to be self-sufficient for 72-hours after a large scale emergency. Keep the home supplies or at minimum water and your documents in a in an easy-to-reach bag in the event that you have to evacuate.

Food and water

- ☐ At least one week of non-perishable, high protein food
- ☐ Three-to five-day supply of water (one gallon per person per day)
- ☐ A manual can opener
- ☐ Food and water for your pets

First aid and sanitary items

- ☐ Sanitation supplies: toilet paper and paper towels, soap, plastic garbage bags and disinfectant
- ☐ Toiletries: toothbrushes, toothpaste, razors, deodorant, feminine products
- ☐ Basic first-aid kit
- ☐ Extra refill of prescriptions
- ☐ Medication
- ☐ Multi-vitamins
- ☐ Bandages
- ☐ Appropriate tape
- ☐ Antiseptic
- ☐ Thermometer
- ☐ Tweezers
- ☐ Scissors
- ☐ Latex gloves
- ☐ Beta dine
- ☐ Hydrogen peroxide
- ☐ Alcohol
- ☐ Anti-bacterial ointment
- ☐ Anti-bacterial soap that does not require water
- ☐ Instant hot/cold packs

Clothing and personal items

- ☐ One change of clothing and footwear and one blanket or sleeping bag per person
- ☐ Contacts or an extra pair of glasses
- ☐ A credit card and cash (small denominations) or traveler's checks
- ☐ Recent photos of family members for identification
- ☐ Important family documents in a waterproof container. Keep the originals of important financial and family documents in a safe place.
- ☐ Special items for infant, elderly or disabled family members

Tools

- ☐ Battery-powered radio
- ☐ Flashlights
- ☐ Extra batteries
- ☐ Waterproof matches and waterproof lighters are essential items.
- ☐ Multi-purpose tool (knife, tweezers, bottle opener)
- ☐ Wrench and instructions to turn off utilities such as gas and water
- ☐ Plastic bucket with tight lid
- ☐ Work gloves
- ☐ Note pad, pen and paper
- ☐ Multi-purpose duct tape
- ☐ Plastic Sheeting
- ☐ Tent
- ☐ Fire extinguisher (ABC type), and be sure everyone knows how to use it and where to find it.
- ☐ An emergency guide, such as a first aid book/chart

Vehicle emergency 'go-kit'

Assemble a smaller emergency 'go-kit' for your vehicle. While your most essential items are water and a full tank of gas, this kit can have many of the same items that you keep in your home except only more compact and in smaller quantities.

Supplies

- ☐ Two to three days of non-perishable, high protein food
- ☐ 2.5 gallons of bottled water
- ☐ Extra medications, such as over-the-counter pain reliever, prescriptions and multi-vitamins
- ☐ First aid supplies: prescriptions, medication, bandages, antiseptic, thermometer, tweezers, scissors and anti-bacterial soap that does not require water
- ☐ Paper towels and tissues

Clothing and protective gear

- ☐ Old pair of eyeglasses or extra disposable contacts
- ☐ Wool blanket and/or sleeping bag
- ☐ Rain gear: poncho and/or umbrella

Tools

- ☐ Signal aids-flashlight, flares, reflectors, matches/lighter
- ☐ Flashlight with extra batteries
- ☐ Battery-powered radio
- ☐ Multi-use tool: knife, bottle opener, tweezers
- ☐ Spare gasoline can
- ☐ Spark plugs
- ☐ Tire change tools: spare tire, jack
- ☐ Tow strap, cable or chain
- ☐ Auto fire extinguisher
- ☐ Multi-purpose duct tape
- ☐ Watertight container
- ☐ Empty gas canister
- ☐ Tarp
- ☐ Pencil and paper

Index